199-222
442

**CLASSIC RESEARCHES IN ORGANIC CHEMISTRY**

*Series Editor* · HAROLD HART, MICHIGAN STATE UNIVERSITY

# FROM VITAL

# STRUCTURAL

CLASSIC RESEARCHES IN ORGANIC CHEMISTRY

O. THEODOR BENFEY · EARLHAM COLLEGE

# FORCE TO

# FORMULAS

**HOUGHTON MIFFLIN COMPANY · BOSTON**

NEW YORK · ATLANTA · GENEVA, ILL. · DALLAS · PALO ALTO

QD
476
.B45F
1964

Cover photo: Molecular model of chlorophyll a.

To Rachel

# EDITOR'S INTRODUCTION

The accelerated pace of scientific discovery which characterizes our time has necessarily eliminated the historical approach to the study of science. Elementary texts in chemistry and physics cannot detail the often tortuous arguments, hypotheses, and experiments upon which currently accepted theories and facts are built. The result is often simply an outline of where we stand today, with only a few cogent arguments or supporting experiments enumerated. During the continuous distillation and condensation (which, indeed, are necessary to prevent elementary texts from becoming encyclopedic), many discoveries, when described in textbook fashion, lose their freshness.

But scientific discovery is a thrilling and exciting process, and a zest for it should be imparted to the beginning student. This series of paperbacks was initiated with the view that much might be done toward this end if the beginner could read about key discoveries in science in the words of the men who wrote of them. The research worker who contributes to the advancing front of science must read of discoveries as they appear in the scientific journals; he cannot wait until they become the subject matter of textbooks. It would seem advisable, then, to introduce the neophyte to the original literature as early in his scientific career as possible. The difficulty encountered in doing this lies in the student's lack of a suitable background necessary for him to profit from being turned loose amongst the journals with a list of references to read. Indeed, he may be dissuaded altogether from the sciences if subjected to such a "trial by fire" procedure. It was therefore decided that original papers, or portions thereof, be selected and presented with sufficient editorial comment to set the stage for each paper and to clarify passages which might be troublesome to the beginner. For the most part, the great scientists are allowed to speak for themselves.

In this volume, Professor Benfey has traced the development of organic structural theory. Here the inquiring and curious student will find the answer to his question: "But how do we know, or how was it deduced, that molecule A has that particular structure and no other?" And he will find the answer told in a form as fascinating and suspenseful as any detective novel. I heartily commend this little volume to all who are curious, and particularly to students of organic chemistry as excellent supplementary reading.

HAROLD HART
East Lansing, Mich.

vi

# PREFACE

This book was begun in 1955 while the author was on sabbatical leave from Haverford College, working with Frank H. Westheimer at Harvard University. Leonard K. Nash of Harvard proposed the study. The suggestion was accepted because the idea was intriguing — to trace down a simple set of concepts, preferably to their origins. The origins, of course, were not found. Discovered were glimpses of a development, the grappling of capable and curious minds with stubborn facts, the introduction of new ways of looking at experimental data, ways borrowed from geometry or linguistics or architecture. Constant throughout the development was the steady growth of experimental data. The accumulators of scientific facts are the unsung heroes of the history of science. Without their labors few new scientific ideas would be established. A single exception does not topple a theory. Only when the exceptions become numerous does the demand become strong for a new viewpoint, one which sees the former exceptions as exemplars of a new principle. A ray of optimism may perhaps be gained from any study of the history of science, because the new principles always seem to be found when needed. Ernst Cassirer expressed it thus: "Every expansion of knowledge due to the steady increase of observational data and the refinements of measuring instruments meets with a corresponding characteristic simplification. The richer the empirical material, the more easily and readily does it allow itself to be fitted into a few great basic forms." A vision of chaos is only a sign of ignorance; rather it should act as a spur to creative labor.

For the sake of continuity and ease of reading I have omitted the horizontal lines through the symbols C, O, and S, which Kekulé used in his papers, quoted here, when he wrote formulas containing carbon, oxygen, and sulfur. The reasons for this usage were complex and not of great importance for our story. In addition to some translations from foreign languages, I have taken the liberty to translate some words from the English chemical vocabulary of the middle nineteenth century into current modern usage, namely *ether* in place of *æther,* and *ethyl* and *methyl* instead of *æthyle* and *methyle* in the Williamson quotations of Chapter 6.

A preliminary version was used in classes at Earlham College. James B. Conant, F. L. Holmes, Leonard K. Nash of Harvard University, Aaron J. Ihde of the University of Wisconsin, and George W. Wheland of the University of Chicago read that version and supplied helpful suggestions, many of which have been incorporated into the present text.

The historical studies underlying this book were supported through several summers by a grant (G4207) from the National Science Foundation. They were carried out at Earlham College and at the libraries of Cincinnati, Harvard, and Vienna Universities. The manuscript was completed during a sabbatical from Earlham College and spent in Washington, D.C. It was typed and retyped by Lucille Rice and her staff in the Earlham Chemistry Department. Christopher, Philip, and Stephen Benfey helped in the reading of proof and Kate Korfer in the preparation of the index.

To Laurence Strong, head of the Earlham Chemistry Department; to Landrum Bolling, President of Earlham College; to the editorial staff of the Houghton Mifflin Company; and to the other persons mentioned in this preface, my warmest thanks.

O. THEODOR BENFEY
Silver Spring, Md.

# ACKNOWLEDGMENT

The author is grateful to the following for permission to use passages originally appearing in their publications: to the Royal Society of Edinburgh for use of the translation of A. S. Couper's paper appearing in "On a New Chemical Theory and Researches on Salicylic Acid," Alembic Club Reprint No. 21; to the *Journal of Chemical Education* for use of the translation of the S. C. H. Windler letter by H. B. Friedman and parts of the Kekulé speech; to The Macmillan Company, New York, and Gerald Duckworth and Company, Ltd., London, for use of the translation of the Dumas passage from A. Findlay's *A Hundred Years of Chemistry;* to The Macmillan Company, New York, and Macmillan and Company, Ltd., London, for use of passages from C. Schorlemmer's *The Rise and Development of Organic Chemistry;* to The Macmillan Company, New York, for use of the Dumas translation from W. A. Shenstone's *Justus von Liebig, His Life and Work;* to Harvard University Press for various passages from H. M. Leicester and H. S. Klickstein's *Source Book in Chemistry;* and to Dover Publications, Inc., New York, for use of passages from Kekulé's paper appearing in the author's *Classics in the Theory of Chemical Combination.*

# CONTENTS

# CHAPTER 1

# Prologue

The problem of communication is becoming acute because each scholarly discipline and subdiscipline, particularly in the sciences, finds it useful or even necessary to develop its own technical language. In this book we shall concern ourselves with the development of one such language, the graphical formulas of the organic chemist. The structures shown below have a beautiful simplicity

$$
\begin{array}{ccccc}
& H & H & H & H \\
& | & | & | & | \\
H-&C-&C-O-&C-&C-H \\
& | & | & | & | \\
& H & H & H & H
\end{array}
\qquad
\begin{array}{c}
Cl \\
| \\
Cl-C-Cl \\
| \\
Cl
\end{array}
$$

ether                        carbon tetrachloride

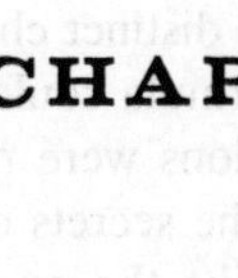

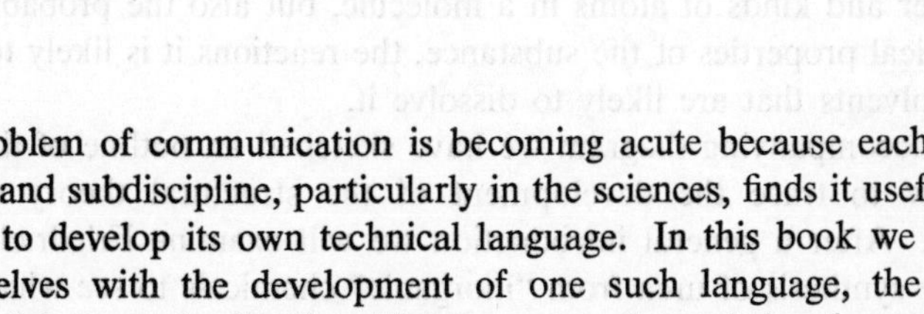

cane sugar

but there was a time, less than a century and a half ago, when many a chemist despaired of ever finding order in the tangled jungle of information concerning the substances derived from living systems. The disentangling process took about thirty years — from the late twenties to the late fifties of the last century. The development of organic chemistry during this period will be studied in detail, culminating in the famous proposals, made independently, in 1858 by the German August Kekulé and the Scot Archibald Couper that it was possible from chemical evidence to represent the pattern of linkages among the atoms in any given molecule. Until then only groupings of atoms, called "radicals," had been identified (groups such as $C_2H_5$ or $C_7H_5O$), but their internal organization, if it existed, was unknown. Once the Kekulé-Couper view was pursued, it became possible to ascribe to a vast number of known organic chemicals formulas like those shown. It was found that, in general, every distinct chemical could be characterized by a separate formula; therefore a formula could serve as a code symbol to identify a given chemical. A few exceptions were noted and their intensive study led to important new insights into the secrets of nature.

Formulas like the one for cane sugar have become an essential means of communication for the chemist. Inspection of a formula tells him not only the number and kinds of atoms in a molecule, but also the probable physical and chemical properties of the substance, the reactions it is likely to undergo, and the solvents that are likely to dissolve it.

In the accompanying diagram we have sketched an outline of the path we will follow to trace the development of the structural theory of organic chemistry. After a general introduction we will examine Friedrich Wöhler's laboratory synthesis of urea from "inorganic" chemicals to see what it reveals about the state of chemistry at the time. His synthesis aroused hope among chemists that other bridges between inorganic and organic compounds might be found. But the formation of urea posed a baffling problem: how could more than one compound have the same molecular formula, that is, be made up of the same number and kinds of atoms? Very early the suggestion was made that these substances must differ in the *arrangement* of their atoms in the respective molecules. By 1832 some chemical reactions were known by which one organic compound was converted into others while retaining unchanged a group of atoms called a "radical." These radicals were first thought of as the "elements" of organic chemistry, but so many of them were soon discovered that organizing principles had to be devised to relate radicals to each other. The manner in which the radicals in a given compound were connected and ultimately the unravelling of the atomic arrangement within the radicals constitute the remainder of our story.

All models, all conceptual schemes have their limitations. No matter how useful a conceptual scheme may have been at a particular stage in the development of a science, sooner or later it is likely to become an obstacle to further progress in the field. In the present study, we shall follow the development of organic chemistry in the nineteenth century in order to understand how the representation of chemicals as formulas of linked atoms came about. In the epilogue we will investigate the difficulties inherent in such a representa-

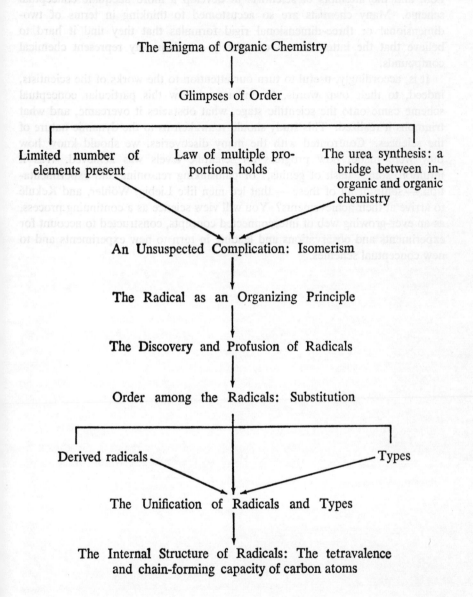

The Enigma of Organic Chemistry

Glimpses of Order

Limited number of elements present

Law of multiple proportions holds

The urea synthesis: a bridge between inorganic and organic chemistry

An Unsuspected Complication: Isomerism

The Radical as an Organizing Principle

The Discovery and Profusion of Radicals

Order among the Radicals: Substitution

Derived radicals

Types

The Unification of Radicals and Types

The Internal Structure of Radicals: The tetravalence and chain-forming capacity of carbon atoms

THE DEVELOPMENT OF THE STRUCTURAL THEORY

tion, and the attempts of scientists to develop a more adequate conceptual scheme. Many chemists are so accustomed to thinking in terms of two-dimensional or three-dimensional rigid formulas that they find it hard to believe that the latter do not completely or adequately represent chemical compounds.

It is, accordingly, useful to turn our attention to the works of the scientists, indeed, to their own words, to understand how this particular conceptual scheme came onto the scientific stage, what obstacles it overcame, and what triumphs it realized. This study should reawaken us to the dynamic nature of the sciences. Confronted with the many discoveries, we should know how they were made, how progress on scientific levels was achieved. Was it intuition, some "flash of genius," or painstaking reasoning and experimentation — some or all of these — that led men like Liebig, Wöhler, and Kekulé to arrive at their achievements? You will view science as a continuing process, as an ever-growing web of interconnected concepts, constructed to account for experiments and observations and leading in turn to new experiments and to new conceptual schemes.

# CHAPTER 2

# The Enigma of

# Organic Chemistry

The recognition of a problem implies a certain amount of prior knowledge. Only when a considerable amount of chemical information had been accumulated did it become apparent that one part of it — what we now call organic chemistry or the chemistry of carbon compounds — did not fit neatly into the general chemical scheme accepted by chemists of the late eighteenth century. The classic distinction between the animal, vegetable, and mineral realms did not suggest any great difficulties that chemists might encounter with the first two. To the chemist of the eighteenth century, however, a marked distinction was becoming apparent between the mineral and organic systems. The former was much easier to study as chemical substances, whereas many organic substances rapidly decomposed as soon as they were removed from the organism and even relatively stable systems were often complex mixtures difficult to separate into their pure component parts. From the work of Lavoisier[1] the axiom was generally established that only pure substances would yield information of significance in the further development of chemistry. Criteria of purity relevant to the organic realm, therefore,

---

[1] Antoine Laurent Lavoisier (1743–1794): Chemist, economist, agriculturalist, and public servant in Paris. He emphasized quantitative aspects of chemical reactions, developed an alternative conceptual scheme to the current phlogiston theory, explained the processes of combustion and respiration as the uptake of oxygen, and was a key figure in the development of modern chemical nomenclature. He was guillotined during the French Revolution ostensibly for his membership in a tax-gathering agency. Lavoisier was Secretary-Treasurer of the Commission that set up the metric system of weights and measures.

5

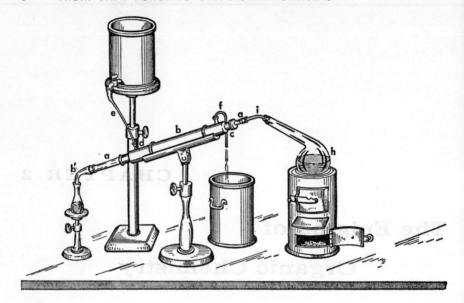

**FIGURE 1**

*Distillation from a retort, using a metal Liebig condenser. After H. von Fehling, Neues Handwörterbuch der Chemie (Braunschweig: F. Vieweg und Sohn, 1875, II, p. 150).*

had to be developed as well as methods for separating chemicals without modifying them. By 1800 a number of general separation methods were known such as distillation and extraction of certain constituents from a mixture by means of water, ether, and other solvents. The medieval retort (*h*, Figure 1) continued to be used for distillation, a water-cooled condenser (*b*) being added early in the eighteenth century to condense the vapors back to their liquid state. After a time the retorts were replaced by flasks (*A*, Figure 2) to which bulbs (*c*) were added to improve the separation of constituents before the most volatile could escape down the sidearm (*a*). Thermometers with a greater range and accuracy were incorporated into the apparatus to keep track of the changes going on inside. In essence the same apparatus is in use today though a Bunsen burner or an electrical heater has replaced the furnace and the condenser is made completely of glass.

## A DEARTH OF ELEMENTS, YET AN ABUNDANCE OF COMPOUNDS

The amalgamation of the vegetable and animal realms was hastened by the discovery that certain chemicals could be isolated from both sources.

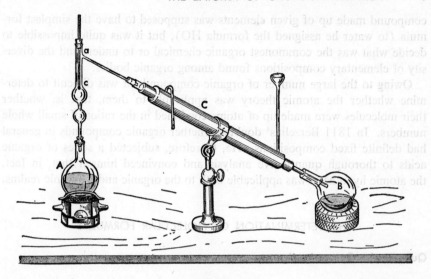

**FIGURE 2**

*Distillation using a Wurtz fractionating tube and a Liebig condenser. After H. von Fehling, Neues Handwörterbuch der Chemie (Braunschweig: F. Vieweg und Sohn, 1875, II, p. 150).*

Thus, Scheele[2] had isolated lactic acid from both sour milk and a vegetable material. He was also successful in isolating a number of other pure organic chemicals, and in the succeeding years other chemists added to this number. Lavoisier studied many such compounds and pointed out that they all contained carbon and hydrogen (because on burning they produced only carbon dioxide and water) and, generally, oxygen, whereas animal matter often contained nitrogen also. It was difficult to understand how such a vast array of differing materials could be produced from only three or four elements.

With the development of Dalton's[3] atomic theory the strangeness of organic chemistry became more apparent, owing to the discovery that the number of compounds formed between any set of three elements other than carbon, hydrogen, and oxygen was extremely small. For Dalton, the commonest

[2] Carl Wilhelm Scheele (1742–1786): Apothecary in Uppsala and Köping, Sweden. He discovered or identified chlorine and oxygen, hydrogen fluoride, hydrogen cyanide, lactic, citric, and other organic acids. He also discovered the adsorption of gases by charcoal and the catalytic effect of mineral acids on the esterification of organic acids.

[3] John Dalton (1766–1844): Chemist, physicist, and meteorologist in Manchester, England. Dalton and the Irishman William Higgins independently applied the atomic conceptions of Galileo, Boyle, and Newton to the elucidation of chemical reactions. Dalton particularly emphasized the weights of atoms. He was also the first to describe the nature of color blindness with which he was afflicted.

compound made up of given elements was supposed to have the simplest formula (to water he assigned the formula HO), but it was quite impossible to decide what was the commonest organic chemical or to understand the diversity of elementary compositions found among organic bodies.

Owing to the large number of organic compounds, it was difficult to determine whether the atomic theory was applicable to them, that is, whether their molecules were made up of atoms combined in the ratios of small whole numbers. In 1811 Berzelius[4] doubted whether organic compounds in general had definite fixed compositions. He, therefore, subjected a series of organic acids to thorough quantitative analysis and convinced himself that, in fact, the atomic hypothesis was applicable both to the organic and inorganic realms.

## THE DETERMINATION OF MOLECULAR FORMULAS

### Quantitative Determinations

In order to assign a formula to a substance, its constituent elements must first be ascertained and their percentage composition determined. If, on burning, only carbon dioxide and water are formed, the original substance must have contained carbon and hydrogen and possibly oxygen. For the *quantitative* determination of these elements, excess oxygen for burning was supplied by potassium chlorate ($KClO_3$) or copper oxide (CuO) mixed with the sample and heated. The water evolved was absorbed in a weighed tube containing a drying agent such as anhydrous calcium chloride, and a specific absorbent for carbon dioxide was used in an analogous manner. In 1831 Justus Liebig[5] refined the method, which essentially is still in use today, and thus transformed an intricate and time-consuming task of research into a simple student exercise. He introduced the "potash bulbs" (Figure 3) containing potassium hydroxide solution for the quantitative absorption of carbon dioxide (carbon dioxide reacts with potassium hydroxide to form potassium carbonate). Since the percent by weight of carbon in carbon dioxide and of hydrogen in water was known, the amount of carbon and hydrogen in the original sample could be determined. A method for nitrogen

---

[4] Jöns Jakob Berzelius (1779–1848): Professor of Chemistry at Stockholm, Sweden. He discovered selenium, silicon, and thorium. He pioneered in the determination of atomic weights and thereby helped establish the atomic theory in chemistry. Berzelius proposed the system of symbols currently in use for the designation of the elements. A prolific writer of textbooks, annual reviews, and articles, his support of, or opposition to, new chemical theories wielded enormous influence among chemists.

[5] Justus Liebig (1803–1873): Professor of Chemistry at Giessen and at Munich, Germany. He established one of the earliest chemical teaching laboratories and contributed to analytical techniques, the elucidation of numerous organic reactions, and the application of chemistry to nutrition and agriculture. He pioneered the use of artificial fertilizers and the extraction of meat juices for food.

**FIGURE 3**

*Liebig's potash bulbs for the absorption of carbon dioxide. After H. von Fehling, Neues Handwörterbuch der Chemie (Braunschweig: F. Vieweg und Sohn, 1875, I, p. 468).*

determination was developed by Dumas,[6] and any difference between the C, H, and N content and the weight of the original sample was ascribed to oxygen, in the absence of indications that other elements were present.

The formula of the compound was then ascertained as follows: If we look at the formula of alcohol, $C_2H_6O$, and use $C = 12$, $H = 1$, $O = 16$ for the atomic weights, then the percent of carbon must be

$$\frac{2 \times 12}{(2 \times 12) + (6 \times 1) + 16} \times 100 = \frac{24}{46} \times 100 = 52\%$$

Similarly, the percent of hydrogen is $\frac{6}{46} \times 100$ and that of oxygen $\frac{16}{46} \times 100$.

The reverse procedure is used if we seek to determine the formula from the percentage composition. Suppose a combustion analysis of acetic acid gave the percent carbon as 40.05 and hydrogen as 6.65. In the absence of other elements, the difference from 100, or 53.30%, must be the oxygen content. These percentages must correspond to ratios of small whole numbers of atoms. If $p$ is the number of carbon atoms and $q$ the number of hydrogen atoms, then the ratio

$$\frac{\text{weight of carbon}}{\text{weight of hydrogen}} = \frac{p \times 12}{q \times 1}$$

Thus

$$\frac{p \times 12}{q \times 1} = \frac{40.05}{6.65}$$

[6] Jean Baptiste André Dumas (1800–1884): Professor of Chemistry in Paris, teacher of Laurent, and at one time French Minister of Agriculture. He devised a method for determining molecular weights, synthesized nitriles, organic nitrates, and trichloracetic acid, and is noted particularly for his studies of substitution of hydrogen by chlorine in organic compounds.

or
$$\frac{p}{q} = \frac{40.05 \times 1}{6.65 \times 12} = \frac{40.05}{79.80} = \frac{1}{2} \text{ approximately}$$

Since the ratio must be one of small whole numbers, the ratio of carbon to hydrogen atoms is 1 to 2, the deviation from this value being ascribed to experimental error. Similarly, the ratio of hydrogen to oxygen atoms is found to be 2 to 1; hence, the simplest formula for acetic acid is $CH_2O$. This is known as its empirical formula. Other formulas of the type $(CH_2O)_x$ where $x$ is a whole number would, of course, correspond to the same percentage composition. The actual formula may be $CH_2O$ or $C_2H_4O_2$, $C_3H_6O_3$, and so on.

Chemists used a number of devices for determining the actual or molecular formulas. One method applicable to acids and bases can be explained in terms of the acetic acid example. This acid forms a sodium salt when treated with sodium hydroxide. Its empirical formula can be shown to be $NaC_2H_3O_2$. Since this formula contains only one sodium atom, it cannot be halved and it is, therefore, extremely unlikely that acetic acid has the simplest formula $CH_2O$. If it were $C_2H_4O_2$, neutralization with sodium hydroxide would involve the simple replacement of one hydrogen by sodium, a process generally found in acid-base neutralizations. On the other hand, sodium acetate may have the formula $Na_2C_4H_6O_2$. The assumption is now made that, if this is in fact the formula, a monosodium salt, $NaC_4H_7O_2$, should not be difficult to find. In addition, a mixed sodium and potassium salt, $NaKC_4H_6O_2$, should be easily prepared in the laboratory. Neither the monosodium nor the mixed salt has ever been found and for this reason the simpler formula, $NaC_2H_3O_2$, is accepted for sodium acetate and $C_2H_4O_2$ for acetic acid.

## The Hypothesis of Avogadro and Ampère

A second method was based on the hypothesis of the Italian A. Avogadro[7] (1811) and the Frenchman A. M. Ampère[8] (1814) that equal volumes of all gases under the same conditions of temperature and pressure contain the same number of molecules. The hypothesis was intended to reconcile Dalton's atomic theory with the simple volume relations found for gas reactions by J. L. Gay-Lussac. Thus:

2 volumes hydrogen + 1 volume oxygen → 2 volumes steam

1 volume hydrogen + 1 volume chlorine → 2 volumes hydrogen chloride

[7] Amadeo Avogadro (1776–1856): Physicist, lawyer, and Professor of Mathematical Physics at Turin, Italy. He was the first to distinguish between atoms and molecules of elements, but his views were long ignored.

[8] André Marie Ampère (1775–1836): Physicist and mathematician in Paris. He discovered the forces exerted by one electric current on another and developed a mathematical theory to account for his observations. The ampere, a unit of current in electricity, was named in his honor.

The hypothesis, however, led to conclusions that were difficult for chemists to accept at the time, in particular to the demand that hydrogen, oxygen, chlorine, and nitrogen gases consisted of diatomic molecules, $H_2$, $O_2$, $Cl_2$, and $N_2$. This claim was denied by Dalton because it conflicted with his principle of simplicity, according to which formulas should be the simplest possible. It was also rejected by others, including Berzelius, since no force could be conceived that would lead to the attraction of two identical atoms. The hypothesis was slowly accepted mainly because alternatives led to greater confusion. It was not until 1860, through the efforts of Avogadro's countryman Stanislao Cannizzaro[9] that the hypothesis was finally presented in a thoroughly convincing manner and soon accepted as the standard approach to the determination of molecular and atomic weights.

If equal volumes of gases contain equal numbers of molecules, the relative weights of equal volumes (that is, their relative vapor densities) must be in the ratio of the weights of their molecules. If the weight of one molecule is arbitrarily assigned (e.g. 32 for $O_2$), other molecular weights can be easily determined by reference to this standard. Since many organic compounds were easily vaporized, a number of organic chemists in the 1830's and 1840's determined molecular weights and hence molecular formulas on the assumption that Avogadro's hypothesis was valid at least for organic compounds.

## COHESION FROM ELECTRICITY

Early in the nineteenth century, Berzelius developed an electrochemical theory of compound formation and stability that was remarkably successful in correlating a large body of inorganic chemistry. However, it was quite incapable of explaining the behavior of organic compounds; thus either a new theory designed specifically for the organic realm had to be developed, or Berzelius' theory had to be extended in such a way as to be applicable to both types of compounds. The latter, as we shall discover, was not an easy task.

After the invention of the voltaic pile, which made possible the production of electric currents for experimental purposes, the effect of electricity on molten materials and solutions was studied extensively. It was found that the metallic constituents of salts generally migrate to one pole or electrode while the nonmetals migrate to the other. Lavoisier's discovery that oxides of nonmetals were acidic whereas oxides of metals were basic could thus be correlated with the electrical nature of these elements.

[9] Stanislao Cannizzaro (1826–1910): Professor of Chemistry in Genoa, Palermo, and Rome. Prior to his chemical studies he studied medicine and physiology. He was exiled to Paris for his support of the abortive Garibaldi revolution in 1847. He was the first to prepare cyanamide ($NH_2CN$); also made extensive studies on aromatic aldehydes including the "Cannizzaro Reaction" of aldehydes with bases.

**Dualism**

Berzelius proposed that all compound formation is due to attraction between opposite electrical charges. His theory, accordingly, became known as the *dualistic* theory. In sodium chloride, sodium was positive and chlorine negative, the attraction of opposite charges accounting for the stability of the salt. In the more complex case of sodium sulfate, the argument went somewhat as follows: Sodium, being strongly positive, attracts and combines with the most electronegative element oxygen to form sodium oxide $Na_2^+O^-$. Sulfur also being electropositive forms $S^+O_2^-$ and $S^+O_3^-$. The further reaction of $Na_2O$ and $SO_3$ to form $Na_2SO_4$ is due to excess charges on the two oxides. Since the strongly positive character of sodium is not completely neutralized by the negative oxygen, sodium oxide retains some positive character. On the other hand, sulfur is not able to neutralize oxygen's negative character completely; thus a residual negative charge remains on sulfur trioxide. The two oxides can combine further to form sodium sulfate $Na_2O^+.SO_3^-$. Even here, it seems, the neutralization is not complete, since sodium sulfate is capable of forming complex salts such as alum, $Na_2SO_4.Al_2(SO_4)_3.24H_2O$.

## THE ENIGMA OF ORGANIC CHEMISTRY

When chemists attempted to apply Berzelius' conceptual scheme, so eminently successful with inorganic compounds, to the facts of organic chemistry, they were completely baffled. They found that a group of four elements gave rise to an enormous number of compounds having a wide range of composition and often of remarkable stability in spite of the fact that only a narrow range of composition can lead to the maximum electrical neutralization. In inorganic chemistry one or, at most, only a few compounds composed of any two or three elements were known, whereas in organic chemistry the situation was very different.

This failure of the dualistic scheme and the complete absence of an alternative explanation of the complex nature of organic compounds led many chemists to believe that they were produced and constructed by a principle unknown in inorganic chemistry and referred to as a "vital force." Since numerous inorganic syntheses had been carried out, but no organic compound had ever been prepared from inorganic materials or from the elements in the laboratory (excluding compounds such as carbon dioxide, assumed to be the final "dead" decay product of living systems), it was thought that organic syntheses could only be performed through the agency of this vital force. Thus, few, if any, chemists deliberately attempted the synthesis of an organic compound. Only the chance production of such a substance was to indicate to chemists the possibility that the gulf between inorganic and organic compounds might not be as immense as they had imagined.

## SUGGESTED READINGS

Findlay, A. *A Hundred Years of Chemistry*, Chapter 1. New York: The Macmillan Company, 1937.

MacNevin, W. M. "Berzelius — Pioneer Atomic Weight Chemist," *Journal of Chemical Education*, **31**, 207 (1954).

Madras, S. "The Historical Approach to Chemical Concepts," *Journal of Chemical Education*, **32**, 593 (1955).

Nash, L. K. *The Atomic-Molecular Theory*. (Harvard Case Histories in Experimental Science, ed. J. B. Conant, Vol. **I**, Chapter 4.) Cambridge: Harvard University Press, 1957.

Parravano, N. "Cannizzaro and the Atomic Theory," *Journal of Chemical Education*, **4**, 836 (1927).

# CHAPTER 3

# The Laboratory Preparation of

# Urea — A Breakthrough

# In Organic Chemistry

A significant breakthrough into the mysteries of organic chemistry occurred through the unintentional production of a compound, hitherto considered organic, from substances easily fitting into Berzelius' dualistic scheme.

FRIEDRICH WÖHLER,[1] a former student of Berzelius and for most of his life Professor of Chemistry at the University of Göttingen, published in 1828 in *Poggendorff's Annalen der Physik und Chemie* a paper entitled "On the artificial Production of Urea":

▼    "In a brief earlier communication . . . I stated that by the action of cyanogen [$C_2N_2$] on aqueous ammonia, besides several other products, there are formed oxalic acid and a crystallizable white substance which is certainly not cyanate of ammonia [$NH_4CNO$], but which one nevertheless always obtains when one attempts to combine cyanic acid with ammonia, for instance by so-called double decomposition."[2]    ▲

---

[1] Friedrich Wöhler (1800–1882): Professor of Chemistry at Göttingen, Germany, student of Gmelin and Berzelius, and a close friend of Liebig. In addition to his extensive studies in organic chemistry, he isolated aluminum and beryllium, prepared calcium carbide and silane ($SiH_4$), and demonstrated close analogies between the chemistry of carbon and silicon.

[2] F. WÖHLER, *Poggendorff's Annalen der Physik und Chemie*, 12, 253 (1828); trans. in *Quarterly Journal of Science*, 25, 491 (1828), reprinted in H. M. Leicester and H. S. Klickstein, *A Source Book in Chemistry* (New York: McGraw-Hill Book Company, Inc., 1952; Cambridge: Harvard University Press, 1963), p. 309. Hereafter cited as *Source Book.*

In this paper Wöhler goes on to report his discovery that the "crystallizable white substance" was in fact urea, a material known only as a by-product of metabolism, as a constituent of urine.

## OXALIC ACID FROM CYANOGEN

The "earlier communication" referred to by Wöhler had appeared in Sweden in 1824 and in Germany a year later. In this article he reported the preparation of oxalic acid, $H_2C_2O_4$, from materials that can be made from the elements (such as cyanogen, $C_2N_2$, prepared by Scheele from carbon and nitrogen some years earlier) or from other inorganic sources. Oxalic acid, a constituent of rhubarb, spinach, and other vegetables, is now classified as an organic compound.

Why then was not the synthesis of oxalic acid hailed as the true breakthrough? It is likely that oxalic acid, being an acid, was considered to fit easily into Berzelius' dualistic scheme. Since it combines with bases to form salts, it reacts similarly to sulfuric acid. If we use modern formulas, the two acids can be shown to react with sodium hydroxide as follows:

Sulfuric Acid:
$$H_2SO_4 + NaOH \rightarrow NaHSO_4 + H_2O$$
$$NaHSO_4 + NaOH \rightarrow Na_2SO_4 + H_2O$$

Oxalic acid:
$$H_2C_2O_4 + NaOH \rightarrow NaHC_2O_4 + H_2O$$
$$NaHC_2O_4 + NaOH \rightarrow Na_2C_2O_4 + H_2O$$

Now carbon dioxide, the final product of oxidation of carbon compounds by combustion or in metabolic processes, was considered a "normal" compound obeying the laws of inorganic chemistry. As an oxide of a nonmetal it combines with water to form carbonic acid, $H_2CO_3$, which is neutralized by bases. Hence, it was not unreasonable to consider oxalic acid also "normal" or, at most, on the borderline between organic and inorganic compounds.

## UREA FROM SALTS

A laboratory preparation of urea, on the other hand, posed an entirely different problem, first, because urea was not in any obvious sense an acid, base, or salt; second, because it had the same composition as the normal salt expected from the synthesis, namely ammonium cyanate; and third, because as a compound of nitrogen it might be considered to belong with a striking group of characteristically organic compounds — the alkaloids — like strychnine, then recently discovered.

Wöhler tells us that the crystalline solid was not only prepared from cyanogen and ammonia but also by "so-called double decomposition." This term refers to the production of a desired substance usually from two salts by an exchange of parts, one providing the acidic and the other the basic part. The reaction will go to completion if the other acid and base fragments combine and precipitate from solution, or if the desired product precipitates. For example, since silver chloride has a very low solubility, lithium nitrate may be prepared by combining aqueous solutions of lithium chloride and silver nitrate.

$$LiCl + AgNO_3 \rightarrow LiNO_3 + AgCl\downarrow$$

Wöhler attempted unsuccessfully to prepare ammonium cyanate by a similar reaction by combining sal ammoniac (ammonium chloride, $NH_4Cl$) with silver cyanate ($AgCNO$):

$$NH_4Cl + AgCNO \rightarrow NH_4CNO + AgCl\downarrow$$
ammonium cyanate
(expected product)

Instead of the expected ammonium cyanate, he obtained urea! WÖHLER thus reports on his experiment:

▼    "The fact that in the union of these substances they appear to change their nature, and give rise to a new body, drew my attention anew to this subject, and research gave the unexpected result that by the combination of cyanic acid with ammonia, urea is formed, a fact that is more noteworthy inasmuch as it furnishes an example of the artificial production of an organic, indeed a so-called animal substance, from inorganic materials. . . .

"The above-mentioned white crystalline substance is best obtained by the decomposition of cyanate of silver with sal ammoniac solution or of cyanate of lead by aqueous ammonia. In the latter way I prepared for myself the not unimportant amounts employed in this research. I obtained it in colorless, clear crystals often more than an inch long in the form of slender four-sided, dull-pointed prisms."[3]    ▲

(A portion of this original synthetic urea is still on view in Munich's Museum of Science and Technology, the Deutsches Museum.)

## UREA: QUALITATIVE OBSERVATIONS

At first, Wöhler studied the extent to which this new compound differed from the expected ammonium cyanate. It was known that ammonium salts

[3] *Source Book,* p. 310.

normally liberate ammonia when reacted with bases. Thus ammonium chloride reacts with sodium hydroxide:

$$NH_4Cl + NaOH \rightarrow NH_3 \uparrow + NaCl + H_2O$$

Cyanates, on the other hand, react with strong acids to liberate cyanic acid. For instance,

$$KCNO + HCl \rightarrow KCl + HCNO \uparrow$$

And by a more complicated route carbonic acid ($H_2CO_3$) and its decomposition product, carbon dioxide, are liberated also. Under suitable conditions cyanates can be precipitated as lead and silver cyanates. WÖHLER reports as follows:

▼    "With caustic potash [KOH] or lime [CaO or, in presence of water, $Ca(OH)_2$] this substance evolved no traces of ammonia; with acids it showed none of the breakdown phenomena of cyanic acid salts, namely, evolution of carbonic acid and cyanic acid; neither would it precipitate lead and silver salts as genuine cyanic acid salts do; it could, therefore, contain neither cyanic acid nor ammonia as such. Since I found that by the last-named method of preparation [the reaction of lead cyanate with ammonia: $Pb(CNO)_2 + 2NH_3 + H_2O \rightarrow PbO + 2CN_2H_4O$] no other product was formed and that the lead oxide was separated in a pure form, I imagined that an organic substance might arise by the union of cyanic acid with ammonia, possibly a substance like a vegetable salifiable base [an alkaloid]. I therefore made some experiments from this point of view on the behavior of the crystalline substance with acids. It was, however, indifferent to them, nitric acid excepted; this, when added to a concentrated solution of the substance, produced at once a precipitate of glistening scales. After these had been purified by several recrystallizations, they showed a very acid character, and I was already inclined to take the compound for a peculiar acid, when I found that after neutralization with bases it gave salts of nitric acid, from which the crystallizable substance could be extracted again with alcohol, with all the characteristics it had before the addition of nitric acid. This similarity to urea in behavior induced me to carry out comparative experiments with completely pure urea isolated from urine, from which it was plainly apparent that urea and this crystalline substance, or cyanate of ammonia, if one can so call it, are completely identical compounds."[4] ▲

Wöhler was a brilliant observer and could recall observations made months or years earlier when confronted with similar phenomena. In a letter written

[4] *Ibid.*, p. 310.

in 1863 to his friend Justus Liebig, WÖHLER evaluated his own strengths and weaknesses as a chemist:

▼    "My imagination is pretty active, but in thinking I am very slow. No one is less made to be a critic than I. The organ for philosophical thought I lack completely, as you well know, as completely as that for mathematics. Only for observing, do I possess, or at least I believe I do, a passable arrangement in my brain. A kind of instinct that allows me to become aware of relations among data may well be connected with it."[5]    ▲

The chemistry of the sequence of observations followed by Wöhler is now well understood and can be explained as follows: Urea, $N_2H_4CO$, a very weak base, reacts with nitric acid, $HNO_3$, to form a sparingly soluble salt urea nitrate, $N_2H_5CO^+$, $NO_3^-$, which retains acidic properties. However, in the presence of a strong base, the nitric acid is removed, leaving urea.

$$N_2H_5CO^+, NO_3^- + Na^+, OH^- \rightarrow N_2H_4CO + Na^+, NO_3^- + H_2O$$

Summarizing his *qualitative* study of artificial urea, WÖHLER mentions the work of William Prout[6] as follows:

▼    "I will describe the properties of this artificial urea no further, since it coincides perfectly with that of urea from urine, according to the accounts of Proust, Prout and others, to be found in their writings, and I will mention only the fact, not specified by them, that both natural and artificial urea, on distillation evolve first large amounts of carbonate of ammonia, and then give off to a remarkable extent the sharp, acetic acid-like odor of cyanic acid. . . ."[7]    ▲

## UREA: QUANTITATIVE FINDINGS

Prout had made numerous *quantitative* analyses of substances of organic origin including that of natural urea. He was considered a very able experimentalist even by Berzelius. It was to Prout's analysis that WÖHLER turns in discussing the composition of his synthetic product:

[5] A. W. Hofmann, ed., *Aus Justus Liebig's und Friedrich Wöhler's Briefwechsel* (Braunschweig: F. Vieweg und Sohn, 1888), **II**, p. 149.

[6] William Prout (1785–1850): Physician and Chemist in London. He demonstrated the presence of hydrochloric acid in the stomach and carried out quantitative analyses of numerous organic compounds. In 1815 he put forward "Prout's hypothesis" that all atomic weights are integral multiples of the atomic weight of hydrogen, and that the "atoms" of the elements are aggregates of hydrogen atoms.

[7] *Source Book,* p. 310–311.

▼ "But if the combination of cyanic acid and ammonia actually gives merely urea, it must have exactly the composition allotted to cyanate of ammonia by calculation from my formula for the cyanates; and this is, in fact, the case if one atom of water is added to cyanate of ammonia, as all ammonium salts contain water, and if Prout's analysis of urea is taken as the most correct."[8]    ▲

Now according to Wöhler a molecule of ammonia consisted of two atoms of nitrogen and six of hydrogen. Cyanic acid, following the custom of the time, was written as if it were in an anhydrous form (thus sulfuric acid would be $SO_3$ instead of $H_2SO_4$, carbonic acid $CO_2$ as against $H_2CO_3$) consisting of two atoms of carbon, two of nitrogen, and one of oxygen. If $H_2O$ is added to this formula, one obtains for cyanic acid, $H_2C_2N_2O_2$, or double the formula used today, HCNO. The latter, of course, cannot be written in the anhydrous form by mere subtraction of a molecule of water. If we now add the formulas of cyanic acid, $H_2C_2N_2O_2$, and of ammonia, $N_2H_6$, we obtain $H_8C_2N_4O_2$.

Again turning to Prout's analysis of natural urea, WÖHLER quotes Prout's percentage composition figures in the following table:

▼

|          |        | Atoms |
|----------|--------|-------|
| Nitrogen | 46.650 | 4     |
| Carbon   | 19.975 | 2     |
| Hydrogen | 6.670  | 8     |
| Oxygen   | 26.650 | 2     |
|          | 99.875 |       |

▲

The sum of the first column should read 99.945. The correction was made in the English and French versions of the paper appearing in the same year. The integral atomic ratios in the second column correspond exactly to those that Wöhler deduced for ammonium cyanate above. They are obtained by inspection of the ratios obtained when the weight percentages are divided by the respective atomic weights, or by the method outlined on page 9.

If the weight percentages are divided by atomic weights, the resulting figures should be in the ratios of the numbers of atoms of the different elements in the compound. WÖHLER used Berzelius' most recent atomic weights, relative to the atomic weight of oxygen taken as 100, and obtained the following figures:

8 *Ibid.*, p. 311.

▼

$$N = 88.518$$
$$C = 76.437$$
$$H = 6.2398$$
$$O = 100.000$$

▲

Water, assumed to be $H_2O$, therefore has a weight of 112.479. On carrying out the calculation

$$\text{nitrogen:} \quad \frac{46.650}{88.518} = 0.527$$

$$\text{carbon:} \quad \frac{19.975}{76.437} = 0.261$$

$$\text{hydrogen:} \quad \frac{6.670}{6.2398} = 1.07$$

$$\text{oxygen:} \quad \frac{26.650}{100.000} = 0.267$$

On inspecting these numbers, we find that they clearly correspond to the integral proportions $N:C:H:O = 2:1:4:1$ or, if doubled, $4:2:8:2$. It should be noted that the same integral ratios would be obtained if atomic weights were based on $O = 16$, in which case $H = 1.008$, $C = 12.01$, $N = 14.01$, respectively.

Conversely, we may calculate the percentage composition of the calculated ammonium cyanate formula. By using the latter atomic weights for $H_8C_2N_4O_2$, the molecular weight $8.06 + 24.02 + 56.04 + 32 = 120.12$. Hence, the per-

cent of hydrogen $= \dfrac{8.06 \times 100}{120.1} = 6.71$, of carbon $= \dfrac{24.02 \times 100}{120.1} = 20.00$,

of nitrogen $= \dfrac{56.04 \times 100}{120.1} = 46.66$, of oxygen $= \dfrac{32 \times 100}{120.1} = 26.64$.

Note that these numbers correspond very closely to Prout's experimental figures (see page 19).

The above figures were obtained by a new analytical procedure developed by Prout. Other chemists were still using potassium chlorate, $KClO_3$, to supply oxygen to the organic compound, thereby converting hydrogen to water and carbon to carbon dioxide. The water was absorbed and weighed and the volume of the gaseous carbon dioxide determined. This method worked well with most vegetable substances, but it failed to give accurate data with nitrogen-containing compounds derived from animals, owing to the partial oxidation of nitrogen. Prout found that gently heated copper oxide (CuO) oxidized all carbon and hydrogen to carbon dioxide and water but liberated nitrogen quantitatively as nitrogen gas. The water was absorbed and weighed and, from known analyses of water, the weight of hydrogen was calculated.

The volumes of carbon dioxide and nitrogen were determined separately. Knowing the volume of carbon dioxide, its density, and percentage composition, Prout was able to obtain the weight of carbon in the sample. The oxygen content was obtained by difference.

## THE EMERGING CONCEPT OF ISOMERISM

WÖHLER's concluding comment was characteristically modest:

▼   "I refrain from all the considerations which so naturally offer themselves, particularly those bearing upon the composition relations of organic substances, upon the like elementary and quantitative compounds of very different properties, as for example fulminic acid and cyanic acid [both having the formula HCNO], a liquid hydrocarbon [butylene, $C_4H_8$, discovered by Faraday in 1825] and olefiant gas [ethylene, $C_2H_4$]. The deduction of a general law awaits further experiment on several similar cases."[9]     ▲

We have spent a considerable time discussing analytical data in order to stress two facts of essential importance to the progress of organic chemistry:

Firstly, analytical data stating the weight percentages of the elements present in an organic compound are not obtained by simple direct observation. Hence, they are only as accurate as (1) the analytical method used and (2) the assumed values for the percentage composition of water and carbon dioxide. Even a slight error in either the method or assumed values will result in inaccurate percentages for the other elements present, and thus lead, as frequently happens, to erroneous formulas.

In view of the above considerations, it becomes clear that accurate analyses of organic compounds were the key to the unravelling of the relations between them. Without these analyses it was impossible to assign reliable formulas, and, until the latter were available, it was impossible to be sure that two quite different substances had the same formula. This discovery of the existence of two substances having different chemical properties but the same formula, later termed "isomerism" by Berzelius, paved the way for far-reaching theoretical developments in organic chemistry.

As Wöhler points out, in his concluding remarks, his finding that urea and the expected ammonium cyanate had the same composition, i.e. were isomers, was not the first case discovered. In 1823 Justus Liebig, working in Paris, had reported analyses of silver and lead fulminates. The following year a refined analysis of the silver salt was reported by Liebig and Gay-Lussac. In late 1824 Wöhler reported some researches on cyanates including analyses of silver cyanate and cyanic acid. The properties of these substances differed

9 *Ibid.*, pp. 311–312.

markedly from those of the fulminic acid series, the salts of the latter, for instance, being explosive whereas the former are not. The formula assigned by Wöhler to cyanic acid, however, was identical with that assigned to fulminic acid by Liebig; this was noticed by GAY-LUSSAC[10] who wrote:

---

▼    "Thus cyanic acid, according to these data, would be formed by one atom of cyanogen [$C_2N_2$] and one atom of oxygen; that is to say it is made up of the same constituents and in the same proportions as the acid which Liebig and Gay-Lussac have designated fulminic acid or cyanic acid [cf. page 19]. But the two acids are very different. The derivatives of one detonate violently when lightly struck, while the others have no such property. To explain these differences it is necessary to postulate a different mode of combination among the elements. This is a matter calling for further examination."[11]                                                        ▲

---

Berzelius in his *Jahresbericht,* the annual review of chemistry which he wrote in Swedish and Wöhler translated into German, was skeptical of the identity of the two compounds. He called for examples of other compounds with identical composition. Gay-Lussac's suggestion that isomerism might be explainable by the postulation of "a different mode of combination among the elements" turned out to be a prophetic insight as to the path theoretical organic chemistry was to pursue in the ensuing decades.

In the meantime Liebig prepared his own silver cyanate, analyzed it, and found large deviations from Wöhler's data. Wöhler countered by reinvestigating the subject and demonstrated unmistakably that Liebig's procedure was in error. Three further analyses by different methods confirmed Wöhler's earlier findings.

The second example of identity of composition cited by Wöhler deals with butylene, discovered by Faraday in 1825, and olefiant gas or ethylene. It was later discovered, however, that their molecular weights were different, butylene having twice the vapor density of ethylene (cf. page 11). Their formulas are now written $C_4H_8$ for butylene and $C_2H_4$ for ethylene. Berzelius coined the word polymerism for this phenomenon.

## THE ELUSIVE PRODUCT, AMMONIUM CYANATE

The elusive salt, ammonium cyanate, was finally prepared a few years later

---

[10] Joseph Louis Gay-Lussac (1778–1850): Professor of Physics and Chemistry in Paris. He studied the expansion of gases, carried out gas density measurements, and made balloon ascents to collect air samples and to study the earth's magnetism. He prepared boron and potassium and made important industrial contributions such as the introduction of the "Gay-Lussac tower" in the manufacturing process for sulfuric acid.

[11] J. L. GAY-LUSSAC, *Annales de Chimie et de Physique,* [2], **27,** 200 (1824).

by Liebig and Wöhler working together, and was shown to have the composition predicted for it. BERZELIUS reported on their work as follows:

▼    ". . . ammonium cyanate . . . can be made from its components and . . . is stable both in the solid state, when formed by sublimation, as also in solution, so long as the latter is not evaporated down by heating, for then the components are slowly changed into urea without any precipitate being formed. . . . This circumstance was not discovered when urea was first artificially formed because the transforming effect of the evaporation procedure was not foreseen."[12]    ▲

The artificial production of urea occurred, therefore, through the use of a particular experimental technique, that of concentrating a solution by heating, a procedure considered so commonplace that it was not even mentioned by Wöhler in either the 1824 or the 1828 paper.

Liebig and Wöhler decided to collaborate after the former had returned to Germany to establish a chemical teaching laboratory at Giessen. They hoped, thereby, to counter a possible view, based on their cyanate-fulminate controversy, that they were always in strife. Their collaboration resulted in a lifelong friendship, and their voluminous correspondence, which covers a period of 44 years, provides fascinating insights into the chemical community of that time.

## THE IMPACT OF THE UREA SYNTHESIS

There is no doubt that the urea synthesis provided a powerful impetus to chemists trying to find order in the field of organic chemistry. If *one* bridge between salts and organic compounds can be established others are likely to be found. In his *Jahresbericht* for 1830 BERZELIUS wrote:

▼    "Beyond all question, one of the most unexpected and therefore most interesting discoveries in the field of animal chemistry is the artificial production of urea. The discovery was made by Wöhler. . . . Urea is not ammonium cyanate, but instead its elements have combined with each other in a different way, so that stronger bases no longer lead to the evolution of ammonia and acids no longer liberate cyanic acid. It can therefore be said that this substance has undergone a transition from a compound inorganic atom [molecule] . . . ammonium cyanate, to a compound organic atom. . . . This discovery holds the key to the development of many clearer viewpoints; it shows for instance that the same number of simple atoms,

[12] J. J. BERZELIUS, *Jahresbericht über die Fortschritte der physischen Wissenschaften*, **11**, 81 (1832).

distributed in dissimilar ways in the compound atom, can give rise to the formation of substances with differing properties. We have already begun to find this in other examples, whose dependability, however, will have to be reinforced by other similar ones."[13]                                                        ▲

Also in 1830 the distinguished French chemist DUMAS wrote:

▼     "All chemists have applauded the brilliant discovery by Wöhler of the artificial formation of urea."[14]                                              ▲

and in 1837 LIEBIG added:

▼     "The extraordinary and to some extent inexplicable production of urea without the assistance of vital functions, for which we are indebted to Wöhler, must be considered one of the discoveries with which a new era in science has commenced."[15]                                             ▲

The speed at which organic compounds were being prepared in the laboratory can be gauged by noting that by 1838 WÖHLER and LIEBIG, in a joint paper on uric acid, could proclaim that *all* organic compounds will sooner or later be thus prepared:

▼     ". . . the philosophy of chemistry will draw the conclusion that the production of all organic compounds, as long as they are not a part of an organism, must be seen as not merely probable but as certain. Sugar, salicin, morphine will be prepared artificially. As yet we do not know the methods by which this goal is to be achieved, because the precursors from which these substances develop are unknown to us. However, we shall come to know them.

"We are not dealing with substances whose composition is based on assumptions. We know with positive certainty, in what proportions they are combined, and we know that they are products of familiar forces."[16]     ▲

The synthesis of urea did not of course immediately destroy the dichotomy between the realms of organic and inorganic chemistry. In the first place, urea might, like carbon dioxide, be considered as an end-product of metabolism, on the borderline between organic and inorganic compounds. And WÖHLER, in his letter to Berzelius announcing his synthesis, suggested — perhaps jok-

[13] J. J. BERZELIUS, *Jahresbericht über die Fortschritte der physischen Wissenschaften,* **9,** 266 (1830).

[14] J. B. A. DUMAS, *Annales de Chimie et de Physique,* [2], **44,** 273 (1830); trans. in W. H. Warren, *Journal of Chemical Education,* **5,** 1547 (1928).

[15] J. LIEBIG, in W. H. Warren, *Journal of Chemical Education,* **5,** 1546–1547 (1928).

[16] F. WÖHLER and J. LIEBIG, *Annalen der Pharmacie,* **26,** 242 (1838).

ingly — that a "Naturphilosoph" might say that the vital force was still lingering in the ammonia and cyanic acid:

▼   "This artificial production of urea, can it be considered an example of the formation of an organic substance from inorganic substances? It is significant that for the production of cyanic acid (as well as of ammonia) one must always begin with an organic substance, and a natural philosopher would say that the organic character has not disappeared either from the animal charcoal or from the cyanogen compounds derived from it, and for this reason an organic compound can still be produced from them."[17]
                                                                          ▲

However, even the discovery of a borderline case was important, for heretofore the wall between the organic and inorganic realms was thought to be impenetrable. A marginal region can be explored and many chemists were fascinated by the prospect.

## VITAL FORCE AFTER SYNTHETIC UREA

Berzelius continued to wrestle with the peculiarities of living systems. In the last (5th) edition of his *Textbook of Chemistry* (1847) he develops a view of "vital force" in a way quite analogous to modern conceptions of the origin of life. He makes clear that by the term "vital force" he does not mean that another force needs to be assumed in addition to the commonly known forces operating in inorganic nature, but rather that a set of unusual conditions exists in living systems within which the usual forces perform the syntheses and transformations peculiar to organic chemistry. By this time a number of other preparations of organic compounds from inorganic starting materials had been achieved, notably Kolbe's preparation of acetic acid in 1845. BERZELIUS described his conception as follows:

▼   "In discussing the different manifestations of life, the word life-force (or vital force) is often used. It is most important that the correct conception is obtained as to the intended meaning of the term. In general, it has always been assumed that it was a force introduced into living nature and overcoming those forces by which the basic materials of nonliving inorganic nature are combined. Thus the chemical products in living bodies are assumed to be determined by this new force, and not by the original forces of combination, operative in inorganic chemistry.

   "This view is certainly not correct although apparent supporting evidence is not lacking. We have seen that life is indeed something foreign to matter,

[17] O. Wallach, ed., *Briefwechsel zwischen J. Berzelius und F. Wöhler* (Leipzig: W. Engelmann, 1901), **I**, p. 208; quoted in D. McKie, *Nature,* **153,** 608 (1944).

incapable of emerging by itself out of lifeless matter, and for us, an unfathomable problem. Once introduced into lifeless matter it creates the conditions for development and growth, but how this proceeds is a riddle which we will probably never solve. If by life-force only this capacity of life is meant, then the concept of a force foreign to matter is sound. If the concept, however, is extended to include the assumption that the vital force pushes out and replaces the original forces of matter, so that the latter cease to operate, then one has gone too far; for at times it is possible by experimentation to unite the lifeless fundamental substances into compounds identical with those that are formed through vital processes. For this to succeed it is only necessary to subject the initial substances to those conditions in which the necessary play of the ordinary basic substances can take place. Life and its force only bring forth the conditions for such phenomena, while the phenomena themselves result from the fundamental material forces that are inseparably associated with matter. . . .

"The uneven distribution of electrical forces, light, heat, and chemical reagents thus appear as the circumstances which determine the combination of the elements into the many different forms typical of organic chemistry. The art of experimentation, which makes use of these circumstances, attempts to copy what goes on in living processes, even if it does not succeed in using these conditions in the same way and in as coordinated a manner as takes place in living processes."[18]                    ▲

---

But not every chemist believed that organic laboratory syntheses were possible. As late as 1842 GERHARDT[19] (cf. page 46) was convinced that the chemist only burns, destroys, and analyzes.

---

▼     "In fact no one has been able to prepare uric acid from urea, . . . sugar from alcohol. . . . Here chemistry has been powerless and, if my guess is right, will always be so. . . . I repeat, chemical forces are opposed to the life force. The chemist's activity is therefore exactly opposed to living nature; the chemist burns, destroys and operates by analysis. Only the life force works by synthesis; it builds up again the edifice torn down by chemical forces."[20]                    ▲

---

[18] J. J. BERZELIUS, Lehrbuch der Chemie, 5th ed., trans. into German from the Swedish by F. Wöhler (Dresden and Leipzig: Arnoldische Buchhandlung, 1847), IV, pp. 5–7.

[19] Charles Frédéric Gerhardt (1816–1856): Professor of Chemistry at Montpelier and Strasbourg, France. He discovered anhydrides of monocarboxylic acids and with Auguste Laurent clarified the distinctions between atomic, molecular, and equivalent weights, and set up a comprehensive system of classification for organic compounds.

[20] C. F. GERHARDT, Journal für praktische Chemie, 27, 439 (1842).

But owing to the mounting examples of organic syntheses, GERHARDT too had to modify his view (1854):

▼   "Natural products and the artificial products of our laboratories are links of the same chain, obeying the same laws, as sufficiently evidenced by the numerous artificial preparations which we owe to modern science."[21] ▲

The urea synthesis had two consequences: On the one hand, it brought forcibly to the attention of chemists the possibility of preparing organic compounds in the laboratory; on the other hand, it furnished another puzzling example of two substances, urea and ammonium cyanate, having the same chemical composition but very different properties.

## ISOMERISM — BERZELIUS SUMS UP

In his 1832 *Jahresbericht* BERZELIUS arrived at a mature concept of isomerism and wrote as follows:

▼   "In physical chemistry it has long been taken as axiomatic that substances of the same composition containing the same constituents in the same proportions, must necessarily have the same chemical properties. Experiments of Faraday (*Jahresbericht*, 1827) seemed to show that an exception to this axiom might occur, if two bodies having the same composition differ from each other by one of them containing twice as many simple atoms as the other, although the relative proportion between their elements remains the same. An example of this is seen in the two hydrocarbons, olefiant gas, $CH_2$ [$C_2H_4$], and the other described by Faraday, which is more condensible, and has the composition $C_2H_4$ [$C_4H_8$] and, therefore, a specific gravity twice as great as the former. In this case the identity of composition is only apparent, for the compound atoms [molecules] are distinctly different, the relative number of the elementary atoms being equal, but the absolute number unequal. More recent experiments have now shown that the absolute, as well as the relative number can be equal; yet their combination may take place in such an unlike manner that the properties of bodies having absolutely like composition become unlike. To such a result we have been led only very gradually. Thus I showed some years ago, that two oxides of tin exist, having the same composition but different properties [this turned out to be an error]. Soon after, it was discovered that Liebig's fulminic and Wöhler's cyanic acid had the same composition and the same saturating capacity [i.e. capacity to neutralize bases, cf. page 10. The number of sodium or potassium salts that could be prepared was used as a

---

[21] C. F. GERHARDT, quoted in E. Hjelt, *Geschichte der Organischen Chemie* (Braunschweig: F. Vieweg und Sohn, 1916), p. 42.

means for deciding the molecular weight.] Almost every *Jahresbericht* since then reported an attempt to explain these results through a previously unnoticed dissimilarity in their composition, but without success. . . . Finally, I believe that my own analysis of racemic acid, an acid of organic origin, has decisively proved the absolute identity of composition of two substances of differing properties. Racemic acid . . . has the same composition as tartaric acid; they are composed of the same elements, combined in the same numbers of atoms, and have the same saturation capacity. If one is willing to be drawn into hypothetical speculations concerning such relationships, it would seem as if the simple atoms of which a substance is composed can be put together in different ways. From this it would follow that in addition to the experimentally demonstrated differences in chemical properties, differences in crystal form of their derivatives should be expected; in fact it turned out that the salts of tartaric acid crystallize differently from those of the newly studied racemic acid in spite of the fact that they contain the same numbers of atoms of acid, base and water. We find here a complement to Mitscherlich's remarkable discovery [1819] that substances composed of different elements, but with these elements in the same atomic proportions and arranged in the same way, crystallize together in the same form, or, as we have called it, are isomorphous. [Thus $KClO_4$ and $KMnO_4$ crystallize in the same crystal form; so do $K_2SO_4$, $K_2SeO_4$, and $K_2CrO_4$.] The complement consists in the fact that substances exist which are composed of the same number of atoms of the same elements, but have their atoms arranged in different ways and thus have different chemical properties and different crystal forms. We may designate these substances as heteromorphous. If future research confirms this view, then science has taken a not unimportant step in the development of our theoretical knowledge as to the constitution of substances. Since it is necessary to have definite and as far as possible rationally chosen expressions for stated ideas, I have proposed to call substances of the same composition but differing properties *isomeric,* from the Greek ισομερης (composed of equal parts)."[22]    ▲

## ISOMERS WITHOUT END

In subsequent years the examples of isomerism among organic compounds multiplied enormously, providing, ironically, a much firmer basis for believing in some fundamental distinction between organic and inorganic compounds. Some explanation was clearly needed for (1) the remarkable number of com-

[22] J. J. BERZELIUS, *Jahresbericht über die Fortschritte der physischen Wissenschaften,* **11,** 44–48 (1832); first third trans. in C. Schorlemmer, *The Rise and Development of Organic Chemistry,* rev. ed. (London: The Macmillan Company, 1894), pp. 133–134.

pounds that could be prepared from carbon, hydrogen, oxygen, and nitrogen, as contrasted with other groups of three or four elements and (2) the frequency of isomerism among these same compounds. We now know, for instance, two compounds of formula $C_4H_{10}$, three of $C_5H_{12}$, five of $C_6H_{14}$, nine of $C_7H_{16}$. More than sixty compounds of formula $C_9H_{10}O_3$ are described in Beilstein's *Handbuch der Organischen Chemie* (see page 58). Over a million distinct compounds containing no elements other than carbon, hydrogen, oxygen, and nitrogen have been reported in the chemical literature.

The remainder of this book will deal with the ways by which chemists were able to develop a conceptual scheme which was to aid them characterize every chemical substance by a different formula. We will note how they explored the same path proposed by Berzelius and Gay-Lussac to arrive at an explanation of isomerism, that of designating the arrangement of the atoms within a molecule, which in its mature form became known as the structural theory of organic chemistry. The first step along this path, the discovery of the more stable atomic groupings or radicals within a molecule, will be discussed in the next chapter.

## SUGGESTED READINGS

Benfey, O. T. "Prout's Hypothesis," *Journal of Chemical Education,* **29,** 78 (1952).

Campaigne, E. "Wöhler and the Overthrow of Vitalism," *Journal of Chemical Education,* **32,** 403 (1955).

Glasstone, S. "William Prout (1785–1850)," *Journal of Chemical Education,* **24,** 478 (1947).

Hartman, L. "Wöhler and the Vital Force," *Journal of Chemical Education,* **34,** 141, (1957).

Kurzer, F., and Sanderson, P. M. "Urea in the History of Organic Chemistry," *Journal of Chemical Education,* **33,** 452 (1956).

McKie, D. "Wöhler's Synthetic Urea and the Rejection of Vitalism: a Chemical Legend," *Nature,* **153,** 608 (1944).

Siegfried, R. "The Chemical Basis for Prout's Hypothesis," *Journal of Chemical Education,* **33,** 263 (1956).

Warren, W. H. "Contemporary Reception of Wöhler's Discovery of the Synthesis of Urea," *Journal of Chemical Education,* **5,** 1539 (1928).

# CHAPTER 4

# Radicals: Atomic Groupings
# Of Some Stability

In seeking to understand how the concept of a radical as a significant component of organic molecules was established, we will again focus our attention not on the first but on the most influential paper concerned with the problem.

## GAY-LUSSAC: THE CYANO RADICAL

In 1815 Gay-Lussac published an extensive study of the derivatives of prussic acid. He showed that the cyano radical (now written CN) composed of carbon and nitrogen remained intact throughout a series of chemical transformations. Thus he prepared hydrogen cyanide or prussic acid, HCN; mercuric cyanide, $Hg(CN)_2$; cyanogen, $(CN)_2$; and chlorcyanogen, ClCN. GAY-LUSSAC reported as follows:

▼ "We see from the observations which constituted the object of this memoir that the knowledge of cyanogen [$C_2N_2$] opens a new field of researches, which will not soon be exhausted. This gas when it combines with hydrogen shows us a remarkable example and hitherto unique of a body which, though compound, acts the part of a simple substance in its combinations with hydrogen and metals. It likewise fills up a gap in chemistry, by making us acquainted with a combination of carbon and azote [nitrogen], which was hitherto wanting."[1]  ▲

[1] J. L. GAY-LUSSAC, *Annales de Chimie et de Physique*, **95**, 230 (1815), trans. in T. Thomson's *Annals of Philosophy*, **8**, 113 (1816), reprinted in *Source Book*, p. 305.

Unfortunately, these remarks went unnoticed, as did Wöhler's paper on oxalic acid, because the cyanides and hydrocyanic acid were not considered typically organic compounds. Since they could be viewed as analogous to nitrates and nitric acid, they too fitted into Berzelius' scheme.

## LIGHT IN A DARK PROVINCE: LIEBIG AND WÖHLER

Of a number of researches on which Liebig and Wöhler collaborated, one of the first was a study of the oil of bitter almonds and its derivatives. Their paper "Researches Respecting the Radical of Benzoic Acid" was published in 1832 in Liebig's *Annalen,* and appeared in English two years later, translated by an American student of Wöhler, James C. Booth. LIEBIG and WÖHLER wrote as follows:

▼    "When in the dark province of organic nature, we succeed in finding a light point, appearing to be one of those inlets whereby we may attain to the examination and investigation of this province, then we have reason to congratulate ourselves, although conscious that the object before us is unexhausted. . . . With such a view, let us examine the following experiments, which as . . . regards their extent and connection, present a wide field for cultivation. . . .

"To fix firmly the station from which the inquiry took its rise, we make the general remark beforehand, that in consequence of our experiments, we believe that there is a body composed of three elements, always remaining the same in its behavior towards other agents, and which can be considered not alone as the radical of benzoic acid, but at the same time as the root perhaps with slight variations of a multitude of similar combinations. . . . Suffer us to say that to a certainty we believe a multitude of similar radicals will readily be discovered by calculation and spontaneous changes in the analyses of organic substances, which chemists have undertaken; but here we stop, for science is but little profited by the raising of expectations, as yet unsupported by facts. . . ."[2]    ▲

The above paragraph provides the first hint as to how the multiplicity and complexity of organic compounds might be intellectually mastered. Stable groupings of atoms are to be discovered that retain their identity when chemicals are transformed into others. Chemists soon began thinking of a radical as the organic equivalent of an element, and there arose among some the hope that the number of radicals might be limited as the number of different elements seemed to be limited. This hope was soon shattered, for the number

---

[2] F. WÖHLER and J. LIEBIG, *Annalen der Pharmacie,* **3,** 249 (1832); trans. by J. C. Booth in *American Journal of Science and Arts,* **26,** 261 (1834), reprinted in O. T. Benfey, ed., *Classics in the Theory of Chemical Combination* (New York: Dover Publications, Inc., 1963), pp. 15–16. Hereafter referred to as *Classics.*

of radicals grew so large that a new ordering principle was needed to show the relations among the radicals. This task was to occupy chemists for the next quarter century and its accomplishment will be described in subsequent chapters.

In order to demonstrate the existence of the same atomic groupings in different substances, these substances (a) had to be prepared in a very pure form and (b) had to be analyzed quantitatively with precision. Further, a sufficient number of chemical transformations of compounds into other pure substances had to be found in order to give a firm experimental basis for the radical concept.

## PURE OIL OF BITTER ALMONDS

Wöhler and Liebig's attempts to prepare pure oil of bitter almonds (our benzaldehyde) was complicated by the fact that they could not even use the constancy of boiling point as an indication of purity, since their thermometers did not reach beyond 130°C. We now know that benzaldehyde boils at 179°C. They reported as follows:

▼    "The substance with which we commence our undertaking is the fluid oil of bitter almonds, distinguished from other similar bodies by the property, first rightly investigated by Stange, of being converted in the air, by the absorption of oxygen, into an acid, into the benzoic acid, and which appeared to lay claim to the highest interest from the manner in which it arises from bodies apparently so different. Another peculiarity, which long since drew the attention of chemists and pharmaceutists to the oil, is its containing prussic acid [HCN] . . . .

"The crude oil was carefully mixed with hydrate of potassa [KOH] and a solution of chloride of iron [$FeCl_3$] by strong agitation and then submitted to distillation. The whole of the oil passed over with the water, and perfectly free from prussic acid. By means of a tube, it was separated from the water and redistilled in a dry apparatus over freshly burned powdered chalk [CaO, a desiccant].

"The oil obtained in this manner is pure, free from benzoic and prussic acids and water, perfectly colorless, very fluid, and has a strong refractive power; its odor is but little different from that of the crude oil; its taste is burning aromatic. It is heavier than water, its specific gravity being 1.043. Its boiling point is so high that we could not determine it with our thermometers, which extended not above 130° centigrade. It is easily inflammable, burning with a bright sooty flame."[3]    ▲

[3] *Classics*, pp. 15, 17.

## BENZALDEHYDE: REACTIONS

The collaborators proceeded to describe a number of simple transformations producing the white crystalline benzoic acid, its salt potassium benzoate (also obtainable by neutralizing the acid with potassium hydroxide), and other compounds:

▼    "Urged through a red-hot glass tube, it remains undecomposed. In the air, in moist or dry oxygen, it is entirely converted into crystallized benzoic acid. In the sun's rays this change is remarkably hastened, beginning in the course of a few moments. The same change takes place in the air by the presence of water and potassa [KOH], with the formation of benzoate of potassa. If these experiments be made in a glass tube closed with mercury, the rise of this metal proves the absorption of oxygen.

"Beside this conversion of the oil into benzoic acid, no third body is formed. . . . Heated with the hydrate of potassa, apart from the air, it forms benzoate of potassa and evolves pure hydrogen gas. . . .

"If the oil be introduced into solution of hydrate of potassa in water . . . it is immediately dissolved, and if the air be wholly excluded, a benzoate appears which when potassa is employed, is soon deposited in large shining lamellar crystals. By the addition of water which dissolves the salt, an oily body is separated, which is no longer the oil of bitter almonds. . . .

"From the action of chlorine and bromine, new compounds arise. . . ."[4]  ▲

## BENZALDEHYDE AND ITS PRODUCTS: COMPOSITION

Wöhler and Liebig now describe their preparation of benzaldehyde:

▼    "The composition of this pure oil [benzaldehyde] was ascertained in the usual way by ignition with the oxide of copper. To expel the hygroscopic moisture from the oxide of copper, we have employed in our experiments a small air pump invented by Gay-Lussac. . . ."[5]      ▲

From the analysis of benzaldehyde they obtained a formula containing 14 atoms of carbon, 12 of hydrogen, and 2 of oxygen or $C_{14}H_{12}O_2$ (the modern formula is $C_7H_6O$). On proceeding to the analysis of benzoic acid, they found a discrepancy between their results and those published by Berzelius. The latter had claimed that the formula of benzoic acid contained one more carbon atom than that of benzaldehyde. This was considered most unlikely since mere air oxidation converted the aldehyde to the acid with no side products. Liebig and Wöhler analyzed the acid as $C_{14}H_{12}O_4$, and so informed

[4] *Ibid.*, pp. 17, 18.
[5] *Ibid.*, p. 18.

Berzelius, who repeated his analytical work and recognized his earlier work as being in error. Liebig and Wöhler formulated the benzoyl radical as (14C + 10H + 2O) so that benzaldehyde became (14C + 10H + 2O) + 2H, and benzoic acid (14C + 10H + 2O) + 2O + 2H. They continue:

▼   *"Chlorobenzoyl:* Hydrobenzoyl (bitter almond oil) consists of (14C + 10H + 2O) + 2H. By the action of chlorine, two atoms of hydrogen unite with two atoms of chlorine to form hydrochloric acid, which is evolved. But the hydrogen gives place to two atoms of chlorine according to the following formula:[6]

$$(14C + 10H + 2O) + 2Cl$$                                   ▲

Benzoyl bromide was obtained from benzaldehyde and bromine, whereas benzoyl iodide was made from benzoyl chloride and potassium iodide since it could not be prepared directly from benzaldehyde and iodine. Benzoyl sulfide, benzoyl cyanide, and benzamide resulted from the reaction of benzoyl chloride with lead sulfide, mercuric cyanide, and ammonia, respectively.

A summary of these reactions is given in the accompanying diagram. The formulas clearly demonstrate the existence, through a series of chemical changes, of a constant group of atoms which became known as the benzoyl radical.

### BERZELIUS TEMPERS HIS ENTHUSIASM

BERZELIUS welcomed the new results in a letter published at the end of the article:

▼   "The results consequent upon your examination of the bitter almond oil, are the most important which vegetable chemistry has thus far received, and promise to diffuse an unexpected light over this part of science.

"The circumstance that a body composed of carbon, hydrogen and oxygen, combines with other bodies, particularly with such as form salts, after the manner of a simple body, proves that there exist ternary composed atoms [atomic groupings consisting of atoms of three different elements] . . . and the radical of benzoic acid is the first example proved with certainty of a ternary body possessing the properties of an element."[7]   ▲

However, Berzelius' immediate enthusiasm soon wore off. He realized that a radical containing oxygen was not compatible with Lavoisier's defini-

[6] *Ibid.,* p. 25.
[7] *Ibid.,* p. 38.

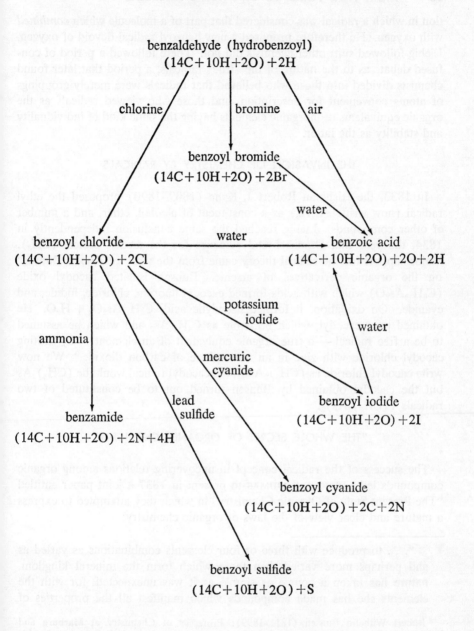

# TRANSFORMATIONS OF BENZALDEHYDE

tion in which a radical was considered that part of a molecule which *combined* with oxygen. He therefore proposed a new benzoyl radical devoid of oxygen. Liebig followed suit; other chemists did not. There followed a period of confused debate as to the nature of the "true" radicals, a period that later found chemists divided into those who believed that radicals were merely groupings of atoms convenient for description, and those who viewed radicals as the organic equivalents of inorganic elements having the same kind of individuality and stability as the latter.

## THE INVASION OF CHEMISTRY BY RADICALS

In 1833, the Irishman Robert J. Kane (1809–1890) proposed the ethyl radical (now written $C_2H_5$) as a constituent of alcohol, ether, and a number of other compounds. Liebig reached the same conclusion independently in 1834, the year that Dumas found evidence for the methyl radical ($CH_3$). Major support for the radical theory came from the work of Robert Bunsen[8] on the organic derivatives of arsenic. Bunsen isolated cacodyl oxide ($C_4H_{12}As_2O$) which with acids formed cacodyl fluoride, chloride, iodide, and cyanide. On oxidation, it formed cacodylic acid, $C_4H_{12}As_2O_3 + H_2O$. He obtained pure cacodyl, which he wrote as $C_4H_{12}As_2$ and which he assumed to be a free radical — a true organic equivalent of an element — by heating cacodyl chloride with zinc in an atmosphere of carbon dioxide.[9] We now write cacodyl chloride as $(CH_3)_2AsCl$; the cacodyl radical would be $(CH_3)_2As$ but the cacodyl obtained by Bunsen turned out to be constituted of two radicals $((CH_3)_2As)_2$.

## "THE WHOLE SECRET OF ORGANIC CHEMISTRY"

The success of the radical concept in uncovering relations among organic compounds led LIEBIG and DUMAS to present in 1837 a joint paper entitled "The Present State of Organic Chemistry" in which they attempted to express a mature and clear view of the laws of organic chemistry:

▼   ". . . to produce with three or four elements combinations as varied as and perhaps more varied than those which form the mineral kingdom, nature has taken a course as simple as it was unexpected; for with the elements she has made compounds which manifest all the properties of

---

[8] Robert Wilhelm Bunsen (1811–1899): Professor of Chemistry at Marburg and Heidelberg, Germany, and teacher of Mendeleev. Although he is best known for his development of the Bunsen burner and of spectrum analysis, he first became famous for his six years of work on the poisonous, explosive, and malodorous organic arsenic compounds.

[9] R. W. Bunsen, *Annalen der Pharmacie*, **31**, 175 (1839); *Annalen der Chemie und Pharmacie*, **37**, 1 (1841); **42**, 14 (1842); **46**, 1 (1843).

elementary substances themselves. And that, we are convinced, is the whole secret of organic chemistry.

"Thus organic chemistry possesses its own elements which sometimes play the role of chlorine or of oxygen in mineral chemistry, and sometimes, on the contrary, play the role of metals. Cyanogen, amide, benzoyl, the radicals of ammonia, of the fatty substances, of the alcohols and analogous bodies, these are the true elements with which organic chemistry operates, and not at all the final elements, carbon, hydrogen, oxygen, nitrogen, which only appear when all trace of organic origin has vanished. . . .

"For us, mineral chemistry embraces all substances which result from the direct combination of the elements as such. Organic chemistry, on the other hand, should comprise all substances formed by compound bodies that function as elements would function.

"In mineral chemistry the radicals are simple; in organic chemistry the radicals are compound; that is all the difference. The laws of combination and of reaction are otherwise the same in these two branches of chemistry."[10]                                                                                    ▲

It was, however, too late. The simple concept of radicals as the organic equivalents of inorganic elements was already being undermined by some intriguing and enormously fruitful experiments that had been performed for a number of years in Dumas' own laboratory.

[10] J. LIEBIG and J. B. A. DUMAS, *Comptes rendus de l'Académie des Sciences*, **5**, 567 (1837); trans. slightly modified from *Source Book*, p. 326.

## SUGGESTED READING

Brown, E. H. "Some Early Thermometers," *Journal of Chemical Education*, **11**, 448 (1934).

Good, H. G. "On the Early History of Liebig's Laboratory," *Journal of Chemical Education*, **13**, 557 (1936).

Oesper, R. E. "Justus von Liebig, Student and Teacher," *Journal of Chemical Education*, **4**, 1461 (1927).

Oesper, R. E. "Robert Wilhelm Bunsen," *Journal of Chemical Education*, **4**, 431 (1927).

Ostwald, W. "Berzelius' *Jahresbericht* and the International Organization of Chemists," *Journal of Chemical Education*, **32**, 373 (1955).

# CHAPTER 5

# The Organization of Radicals:
# Substitution

We noted in Chapter 4 how the attempt to relate those organic compounds that contained the same radical was not a sufficient solution to the complexity of organic chemistry. Owing to their very large number, it became evident that the radicals needed to be related among themselves by some basic principle. The discovery of the substitution theory, that certain radicals in a compound could be transformed into others by relatively simple processes, led to the establishment of this principle.

## CHOKING SMOKE FROM THE TUILERIES CANDLES

A. W. Hofmann (cf. page 55), in his obituary on Dumas,[1] claimed that Dumas himself had told him the origin of the substitution theory, a story that had never before been published. At a royal ball one evening at the Tuileries palace in Paris, the rooms were filled with a highly irritating vapor, which obviously came from some wax candles burning with a smoky flame. Alexandre Brogniart, director of the Sèvres Porcelain Works, when called in for advice, handed the problem to his son-in-law Dumas.

Dumas easily proved that the choking vapors contained chlorine, that the supplier of the candles to the palace had bleached the wax with chlorine gas, leaving residual chlorine in the candles in appreciable amounts. Dumas pro-

[1] A. W. Hofmann, *Berichte der Deutschen chemischen Gesellschaft,* **17,** Referate 667 (1884).

ceeded to test the effect of chlorine on other organic substances, such as oil of turpentine, and showed that part of the chlorine is retained in the organic substance while the rest combines with hydrogen from the compound to liberate hydrogen chloride.

This substitution of hydrogen by chlorine was by no means the first recorded in the chemical literature. We have already seen that Wöhler and Liebig had replaced hydrogen by chlorine in benzaldehyde. Gay-Lussac similarly had obtained cyanogen chloride ($CNCl$) from hydrogen cyanide (1815) as well as chlorinated derivatives from oils and wax and even stated (according to some notes on Gay-Lussac's lectures, published in 1828 without Gay-Lussac's consent) that the chlorine "takes the place of the hydrogen."[2] Finally, Faraday in 1821 had prepared a completely chlorinated hydrocarbon ($C_2Cl_6$) from Dutch liquid ($C_2H_4Cl_2$).

## POSITIVE HYDROGEN AND NEGATIVE CHLORINE

None of these chemists, however, had elaborated a theory on the basis of their findings. Once the radical became the major focus of attention, the chlorination reactions took on a very curious character. If hydrogen in an established radical can be replaced by chlorine, without (as it turned out) significantly changing the properties of the radical, then something quite new in the behavior of chemical compounds was becoming evident. Berzelius had welcomed radicals because their formulation seemed to permit the inclusion of organic compounds in his dualistic scheme. But in his scheme hydrogen was considered to be electropositive, belonging with the metals, whereas chlorine was a typically electronegative element. Now the conception of compound formation advocated by Berzelius rested squarely on the attraction of oppositely charged elements or groups (cf. page 12). How, according to his scheme, was it possible to understand the direct substitution of hydrogen by chlorine without a significant change in the character of the compound? Berzelius refused to accept substitution and rewrote the formulas of his contemporaries with increasingly complicated radicals. But Dumas and more especially his pupil (and later his bitter foe) Auguste Laurent,[3] without understanding the nature of these transformations, accepted the *fact* of substitution and proceeded to propound important laws and generalizations based on this fact. Dumas advanced his speculations slowly, whereas Laurent unhesitatingly developed and expounded his proposals.

[2] Cf. J. L. Gay-Lussac, *Annales de Chimie et de Physique,* [2], **37,** 441 (1828).

[3] Auguste Laurent (1807–1853): Professor of Chemistry in Bordeaux, France, and Assayer of the Paris Mint. He worked with Gerhardt on an extensive systematization of organic compounds to replace the dualistic system of Berzelius. He isolated and characterized anthracene, phthalic acid, and phthalimide, and influenced Pasteur in the latter's early crystallographic studies.

## THE BATTLE OF THEORIES

In 1834 Dumas reported the chlorination of ethyl alcohol to form chloroform ($CHCl_3$) and chloral ($CCl_3CHO$).[4] He also showed that in this reaction chlorine replaced hydrogen, liberating a volume of hydrogen chloride equal to the volume of chlorine used. He stated that when hydrogen is thus removed the compound "appropriates to itself" an *equivalent* amount of the attacking agent. Later this was spelled out to mean that, when an atom of hydrogen is lost, one atom of chlorine, bromine, or iodine, or half an atom of oxygen is gained.

Laurent, from studies suggested by Dumas on the chlorination of naphthalene ($C_{10}H_8$), prepared both substitution and addition derivatives. He was struck by the similarity of these compounds to the original naphthalene and began to put forward the view that chlorine, as Gay-Lussac had already hinted in his lectures, "takes the place of" hydrogen without materially altering the molecule.

In 1838 Berzelius bitterly attacked these views, attributing them to Dumas. This led DUMAS to deny completely any association with these proposals:

▼    "Berzelius attributes to me, an opinion precisely contrary to that which I have always maintained, namely, that the chlorine in this case takes THE PLACE of the hydrogen. I have never said anything of the kind, neither can anything of the kind be deduced from the opinions I have put forward with regard to this order of facts. To represent me as saying, that hydrogen is replaced by chlorine, which fulfills the same functions, is to attribute to me an opinion against which I protest most strongly, as it is opposed to all that I have written upon these matters. The law of substitutions is an empiric law and nothing more: it expresses a relation between the hydrogen expelled, and the chlorine retained. I am not responsible for the gross exaggeration with which Laurent has invested my theory; his analyses moreover do not merit any confidence."[5]                              ▲

The last sentence is curious since even Berzelius had commented on Laurent's "rare talent for research." Laurent accepted full responsibility for his views. In 1835 he had proposed that radicals could be modified by substitution. "I shall call naphthalene the fundamental radical and the compounds which result from its transformation the derived radicals." By the following year he had generalized the new concept to cover the whole of organic

[4] J. B. A. Dumas, *Annales de Chimie et de Physique*, [2], **56**, 113 (1834).
[5] J. B. A. DUMAS, *Comptes rendus de l'Académie des Sciences*, **6**, 647 and 695 (1838); trans. by W. Odling in A. Laurent's *Chemical Method* (London: The Cavendish Society, 1855), p. 199, reprinted in *Classics*, p. 62.

chemistry: "All organic compounds are derived from a hydrocarbon, a fundamental radical, which often does not exist in its compounds but which may be represented by a derived radical containing the same number of equivalents."[6]

## A GEOMETRIC MODEL

In 1837 Laurent successfully presented his doctoral thesis to a committee of the French Academy of Sciences that included among others Dumas and Dulong. He proposed, probably for the first time in the history of organic chemistry, a three-dimensional model for a better comprehension of molecules and their interrelations. Laurent was both an excellent crystallographer (Pasteur was strongly influenced by him in Paris) and an artist, and in these activities we may see the origin of the geometric viewpoint. Although his model was ignored for two decades, geometric reasoning was to play a tremendously important role in future years. In his thesis LAURENT uses the word nucleus instead of radical.

▼     "Let us imagine a four-sided prism [or, for simplicity, a cube], of which the eight angles are occupied by eight atoms of carbon, and the centres of the twelve edges by twelve atoms of hydrogen. Let us call this prism the *form* or *fundamental nucleus,* and let us represent it by

$$C^8H^{12}.$$

"If to the bases of the prism, we apply pyramids or atoms of hydrogen, we shall have a hyperhydride, if of chlorine, a hyperhalyde, and if of oxygen, an aldehyde or acid. We will represent the form and composition of these pyramidal prisms thus:

$$C^8H^{12} + H^2$$
$$C^8H^{12} + Cl^2$$
$$C^8H^{12} + O$$
$$C^8H^{12} + O^2$$

"By certain reactions, we shall be able to slice away the pyramidal portions of the crystal, that is to say, take away its chlorine, oxygen, or excess of hydrogen, and reobtain the fundamental prism.

"Let us suppose that chlorine, put in presence of this simple prism, removed one of the edges or hydrogen atoms; the prism deprived of this edge would be destroyed, unless it were supplied with some other edge, whether of chlorine, bromine, zinc, &c.; no matter what the nature of the edge, provided it succeeds in maintaining the equilibrium of the other edges and angles. Thus will be formed a new or *derived nucleus* [or radical]

[6] A. LAURENT, quoted in C. de Milt, *Chymia,* **4,** 92 (1953).

similar to the preceding, and of which the form may be represented by

$$C^8(H^{11}Cl).$$

"If we put this new prism in the presence of chlorine, we may pyramidise it, that is to say, transform it into a hyperhalide

$$C^8(H^{11}Cl) + Cl^2$$

or we may remove from it another edge of hydrogen. But this must be still replaced by an edge of chlorine, and we shall obtain a new derived prism of which the formula will be[7]

$$C^8(H^{10}Cl^2)$$                                                      ▲

## DUMAS' TYPES

Other workers were discovering reactions in complete conformity with Laurent's ideas. Finally, Dumas himself, when he prepared trichloracetic acid ($CCl_3CO_2H$) from acetic acid ($CH_3CO_2H$) (1838), admitted that the substitution produced very little change in the character of the substance. A chlorinated acid was still an acid, whereas in inorganic chemistry the substitution of an electronegative for an electropositive element in an oxide usually changed that oxide from a base to an acid. But, rather than admit his adherence to Laurent's views, Dumas announced his acceptance of substitution by proposing a new "unitary," as opposed to "dualistic," theory of "types." He implied, thereby, that Laurent was attempting to retain Berzelius' dualistic concept, viewing radicals as organic "elements" and permitting substitution only within these radicals. Dumas proposed substitution in whole molecules rather than in radicals and suggested the use of the term "type" to classify those substances that could be converted into each other without significantly changing their properties. DUMAS wrote that his new chlorinated acid:

▼     ". . . is chlorinated vinegar, but what is very remarkable, at least for those who refuse to find in chlorine a body capable of replacing hydrogen in the precise and complete sense of the word, this chlorinated vinegar is just as much an acid as common vinegar itself. Its acid power is not changed. It saturates the same quantity of alkali as before, and saturates it equally well, and the salts to which it gives rise exhibit, when compared with acetates, resemblances full of interest and generality.

"Here then is a new organic acid, containing a very considerable quantity of chlorine, and exhibiting none of the reactions of chlorine; its hydrogen has disappeared, and has been replaced by chlorine, and yet this remarkable substitution has produced only a slight change in its properties, all its essential characters remaining unaltered. . . .

[7] A. LAURENT, in *Classics*, p. 57–58.

"If its internal properties are modified, this modification becomes apparent only when through the intervention of a new force, the molecule itself is destroyed and transformed into new products. . . .

". . . It is evident that, in confining myself to this system of ideas dictated by facts, I have not in any way taken into consideration the electro-chemical theories on which Berzelius has generally based the idea predominating in the opinions which this illustrious chemist has endeavored to enforce.

"But do these electro-chemical ideas, this special polarity attributed to the molecules [atoms] of elementary bodies, rest upon facts so evident that it is necessary to erect them into articles of faith? Or if they must be regarded as hypotheses, have they the power of lending themselves to facts, of explaining and foreseeing them with so complete a certainty as to have afforded important assistance in chemical researches? We must admit that such is not the case."[8]    ▲

Dumas then refers to Mitscherlich's crystallographic law of isomorphism, that Berzelius had used earlier (cf. page 28) in a somewhat different connection, to point to the generally accepted phenomenon of certain metals and nonmetals replacing each other in crystals without changing the crystal form, as in potassium sulfate, $K_2SO_4$, and potassium chromate, $K_2CrO_4$.

▼    "What has been found in inorganic nature to be a useful and true guide, isomorphism, is a theory which, as is well known, rests on facts, and which, as is equally well known, is little in accordance with the electrochemical theory. Now in organic chemistry the theory of substitution plays the same part as isomorphism in mineral chemistry; and perhaps we may some day by experience find that these two general points of view are intimately related, being dependent on the same causes and capable of being comprised in a common expression.

"For the present, from the transformation of acetic acid into chloracetic acid, from that of aldehyde [acetaldehyde, $CH_3CHO$] into chloral [$CCl_3CHO$]; from the fact that the hydrogen of these bodies is replaced by chlorine, volume for volume, without altering their original nature, we must conclude: *That there exist in organic chemistry certain TYPES which remain as such, even after replacing their hydrogen by an equal volume of chlorine, bromine or iodine;* i.e. the theory of substitution rests on facts, on the most striking facts of organic chemistry."[9]    ▲

[8] J. B. A. Dumas, *Annalen der Chemie und Pharmacie*, **32**, 101 (1839); trans. in W. A. Shenstone, *Justus von Liebig, his Life and Work* (New York: The Macmillan Company, 1895), pp. 59–60.
[9] J. B. A. Dumas, *Annalen der Chemie und Pharmacie*, **32**, 101 (1839); trans. in C. Schorlemmer, *The Rise and Development of Organic Chemistry*, rev. ed. (London: The Macmillan Company, 1894), pp. 41–42.

In another place DUMAS wrote:

▼     "Every chemical compound forms a complete whole and cannot, therefore, consist of two parts [as dualism had asserted]. Its chemical character is dependent primarily on the arrangement and number of its atoms and in a lesser degree on their chemical nature."[10]     ▲

The emphasis on *arrangement,* suggesting a spatial order, reminds us of Laurent's views. The proposal that chemical character is determined more by arrangement and number than by the nature of the elements was a direct declaration of war on the dualistic scheme.

Even though Dumas, by noting the production of chloroform from the sodium salt of trichloracetic acid,

$$CCl_3CO_2Na + NaOH \rightarrow CHCl_3 + Na_2CO_3$$

had predicted and confirmed the possibility of converting sodium acetate into marsh gas (methane)

$$CH_3CO_2Na + NaOH \rightarrow CH_4 + Na_2CO_3$$

and though Melsens in 1842 had reconverted trichloracetic acid into acetic acid with potassium amalgam, Berzelius still refused to accept the theory of direct substitution.

Liebig, on the other hand, accepted Dumas' examples as special cases, but at first would not agree to the generalized theory of types.

### DANGERS OF OVERGENERALIZATION — NIGHTCAPS OF SPUN CHLORINE

When Dumas suggested, on very sketchy evidence, that the law of substitution could apply even to carbon, i.e. carbon also could be replaced by other elements without loss of the essential properties of the type molecule, the concensus of opinion was that he had gone too far. This extrapolation, suggesting that any compound could have all its elements replaced by others, or even one other element, and yet have its chemical character remain unchanged, was greeted by a letter in Liebig's *Annalen,* presumably from Paris and signed S. C. H. Windler.[11] This letter claimed that manganous acetate had been chlorinated atom for atom so that only chlorine (and water of crystallization) was present in the final product, yet the properties of manganous acetate were preserved — the "type" was "conserved." Wöhler had written the letter as a private joke to Berzelius and sent a copy to Liebig

[10] J. B. A. DUMAS, quoted in A. Findlay, *A Hundred Years of Chemistry* (New York: The Macmillan Company, 1937), p. 30.
[11] The German for Swindler is *Schwindler.*

for his amusement, never dreaming that Liebig would publish it. Wöhler's letter is quoted in full as follows:

---

▼ *"Concerning the Law of Substitution and the Theory of Types*

Paris, March 1, 1840

"Sir,

"I hasten to communicate to you one of the most striking facts of organic chemistry. I have verified the theory of substitution in an extremely remarkable and completely unexpected manner. It is only now that one can appreciate the great value of this ingenious theory and that one can dimly foresee the tremendous discoveries which it promises to realize for us. The discovery of chloracetic acid and the constancy of type in the chlorinated compounds derived from ether and from ethyl chloride have led me to experiments which I shall now describe. I allowed a stream of chlorine to pass through a solution of manganous acetate under the direct influence of sunlight. After 24 hours, I found in the liquid a fine crystallization of a yellow salt with a violet tint. The solution contained only the same salt and hydrochloric acid. I have analyzed this salt; it is manganous chloracetate. So far nothing extraordinary, a simple substitution of the hydrogen of acetic acid by an equivalent amount of chlorine, already known from the beautiful researches on chloracetic acid. This salt, heated to 110° in a stream of dry chlorine, was converted with liberation of oxygen gas into a new golden yellow compound, the analysis of which led to the formula $MnCl_2 + C_4Cl_6O_3$ for its composition. There was thus substitution of the oxygen of the base by chlorine, as has been observed in a great many circumstances. The new substance was dissolved in very pure chloral with the aid of heat, and I made use of this liquid, unaffected by chlorine, to continue the treatment by that reagent. I let dry chlorine flow for four hours, keeping the liquid always very near its boiling point. During this time a white material constantly precipitated; this was found on careful examination to be manganous chloride. When there was no further precipitation, I cooled the liquid for some time, and I obtained a third substance in [the form of] silky yellow needles with a green cast. It was $C_4Cl_{10}O_3$, or, in other words, it was manganous acetate in which all the hydrogen and the manganous oxide were replaced by chlorine. Its formula ought to be written as $Cl_2Cl_2 + C_4Cl_6O_3$. There were thus six atoms of chlorine in the acid, the four other atoms representing manganous oxide. Like hydrogen, manganese and oxygen can be replaced by chlorine; one could see nothing surprising in this substitution.

"But this is still not the end of this remarkable series of substitutions. On allowing chlorine again to act upon a solution of this material in water, there was a liberation of carbonic acid, and on cooling the liquid to $+2°$

there was deposited a yellowish mass formed of small plates, closely resembling the hydrate of chlorine. Also, it contained only chlorine and water. But on measuring the density of its vapor, I have found that it was formed from 24 atoms of chlorine and 1 atom of water. Here then was the most perfect substitution of all the elements of manganous acetate. The formula of the substance must be expressed as $Cl_2Cl_2 + Cl_8Cl_6Cl_6 + aq$. Although I know that in the bleaching action of chlorine there is replacement of hydrogen by chlorine, and that the fabrics, which are bleached in England according to the laws of substitution, conserve their type, I believe nevertheless that the replacement of carbon by chlorine, atom for atom, is a discovery which belongs to me. Please make note in your journal and accept, etc.

                                                        S. C. H. Windler"[12] ▲

To this letter LIEBIG added the unsigned footnote:

▼    "I have just learned that in the shops of London there are already fabrics of spun chlorine, very much in demand in the hospitals and preferred over all others for night caps, drawers, etc."[12]
                                                                            ▲

That the substitution theory could be overgeneralized was evident. That it contained important truths could no longer be denied. Some laws must exist which determine what atoms in what numbers and under what conditions can take each other's place. Chlorine, for instance, can never replace carbon without disrupting the molecule, but this could not have been known until the concept of valence, the characteristic combining capacity of each element, was understood.

The years that followed were significant chiefly for a slow clarification of the distinctions between the terms atom, molecule, and equivalent. This was the work mainly of Charles Frédéric Gerhardt and Laurent. This clarification of terms, and its attendant fundamental principles for establishing atomic weights and molecular formulas, were a necessary prerequisite to a large scale systematization of organic chemistry.

## REENTER AVOGADRO

Laurent and Gerhardt were among the first chemists to take seriously the views of Avogadro and Ampère which had been long ignored for reasons

[12] S. C. H. WINDLER (F. Wöhler), Annalen der Chemie und Pharmacie, **33**, 308 (1840); trans. in G. W. Wheland, Advanced Organic Chemistry, 3rd ed. (New York: John Wiley and Sons, Inc., 1960), p. 760, based on translation by H. B. Friedman, Journal of Chemical Education, **7**, 633 (1930).

mentioned earlier (cf. page 10). By 1840, a type of compound formation had been established (by substitution reactions) which was counter to Berzelius' electrochemical viewpoint. Berzelius, who had often been attacked as a die-hard vitalist, refused to believe in this exception to his system, in part, because he viewed it as reintroducing a sharp distinction between inorganic and organic compounds. Thus he wrote:

▼    "Liebig . . . has assumed that the laws which determine the combinations of the elements in inorganic nature, still operate up to a certain point in the organic realm, but that beyond this point quite different laws become determining, which are as yet unknown to us. Certainly, types of combinations occur, whose causes we cannot determine, but this inability is not a sufficient reason on which to base the assumption of a change in the laws of nature."[13]                                                                    ▲

Gerhardt and Laurent, on the other hand, in a sense preserved the unity of organic and inorganic nature by accepting the hypothesis of Avogadro and Ampère that equal volumes of all gases under the same conditions of temperature and pressure must contain the same number of molecules. Thus, chlorine becomes $Cl_2$, and oxygen $O_2$, and a nonelectrochemical form of bonding was introduced even into inorganic chemistry. (This bond is the modern covalent bond as contrasted to the electrovalent bond acceptable to Berzelius. Its mode of attraction was not understood until the advent of wave mechanics around 1925.) Many atomic weights were changed by Gerhardt and Laurent to those in use today, and their formulas for organic compounds became essentially the modern ones. Their reform was less successful in the case of some of the metals, which had to await the clarification by Cannizzaro at the chemical congress at Karlsruhe in 1860.

## PATTERNS AMONG FORMULAS — THE WATER TYPE

When the new organic formulas were studied, some striking resemblances appeared. A paper by LAURENT (1846) commenting on the new method for determining atomic weights and formulas contains the following table:[14]

[13] J. J. BERZELIUS, *Lehrbuch der Chemie*, 5th ed., trans. into German from the Swedish by F. Wöhler (Dresden and Leipzig: Arnoldische Buchhandlung, 1847), IV, p. 40.
[14] A. LAURENT, *Annales de Chimie et de Physique*, [3], **18**, 266 (1846). Excerpts of this article were translated with commentary by T. S. Hunt, *American Journal of Science*, [2], **6**, 173 (1848).

▼

|  | hydrogen acid | hydrogen sulfide acid | sulfurous acid | sulfuric acid | carbonic acid | oxalic acid |
|---|---|---|---|---|---|---|
| Acid | OHH | SHH | $SO_3HH$ | $SO_4HH$ | $CO_3HH$ | $C_2O_4HH$ |
| Acid Salt | OHK | SHK | $SO_3HK$ | $SO_4HK$ | $CO_3HK$ | $C_2O_4HK$ |
| Neutral Salt | OKK | SKK | $SO_3KK$ | $SO_4KK$ | $CO_3KK$ | $C_2O_4KK$ |
| Double Salt | OKM | SKM | $SO_3KM$ | $SO_4KM$ | $CO_3KM$ | $C_2O_4KM$ |
| Vinic acid | OEtH | SEtH | $SO_3EtH$ | $SO_4EtH$ | $CO_3EtH$ | $C_2O_4EtH$ |
| Salt | OEtK | SEtK | $SO_3EtK$ | $SO_4EtK$ | $CO_3EtK$ | $C_2O_4EtK$ |
| Ether | OEtEt | SEtEt | $SO_3EtEt$ | $SO_4EtEt$ | $CO_3EtEt$ | $C_2O_4EtEt$ |
| Anhydride |  |  | $SO_2$ | $SO_3$ | $CO_2$ |  |

▲

where Et = ethyl [$C_2H_5$], M is any metal capable of replacing hydrogen, atom for atom, and acid is used in the very general sense of having a hydrogen that is replaceable by a metal, so that water is called hydrogen acid and ethyl alcohol [$C_2H_5OH$] is a vinic acid or acid of wine.

Clearly Laurent is here emphasizing the fact that all the substances in a given column can be seen as substitution products of the first member of the column. Though he does not use the word "type" to characterize the acids in the first row, the term is used by T. S. Hunt[15] in the American version and commentary published two years later. The chemical types of Dumas had been restricted to compounds of very similar properties such as acetic and chloracetic acids. For this reason the number of independent types was soon to become unmanageably large. H. V. Regnault[16] had further proposed that, in addition to these "chemical types," some "mechanical types" had to be recognized, derivable by substitution but not very similar chemically. Laurent's table ignores this distinction, as well as any distinction between organic and inorganic compounds, and classifies bases (KOH), oxides ($K_2O$), alcohols ($C_2H_5OH$), metal alcoholates ($C_2H_5OK$), and ethers ($C_2H_5OC_2H_5$) as all belonging to the *water type*. To these T. S. Hunt added oxygen acids such as HOCl. The break with Berzelius was now complete. Instead of regarding potassium hydroxide as the hydrate of $K_2O$ (i.e. $K_2O.H_2O$), it becomes a substitution product of water (KOH), which is certainly plausible

[15] Thomas Sterry Hunt (1826–1892): Professor of Chemistry in Quebec and Montreal and Professor of Geology at the Massachusetts Institute of Technology. He was president of the American Chemical Society in 1879 and 1888. His main interests were in mineralogical and theoretical chemistry. He invented the green ink widely used in the printing of greenback currency.

[16] Henri Victor Regnault (1810–1878): Professor in Paris and Director of the Sèvres Porcelain Factory. He carried out accurate determinations of the expansion and compressibility of gases and liquids and made extensive studies on the reactions of alkyl halides.

from experimental evidence since potassium replaces hydrogen in water with considerable violence as shown:

$$2K + 2H_2O \rightarrow 2KOH + H_2$$

Like Berzelius, Liebig had considered ethyl alcohol as the hydrate of ethyl ether, assigning ether the formula $C_4H_{10}O$ so that alcohol became $C_4H_{10}O.H_2O$. According to this view both ether and alcohol contained the same single radical $C_4H_{10}$. Laurent, on the other hand, wrote $C_2H_5OC_2H_5$ for ether and $C_2H_5OH$ for alcohol. This paper by Laurent may well be considered the turning point in the development of modern chemical formulas. What Laurent had done was to incorporate radicals into the types, whereas previously radicals had been used to perpetuate the dualistic system. He further suggested very simple compounds as the fundamental types, in which hydrogen was replaceable by either elements or radicals. In fact his whole table may be considered as belonging to the *water type* if we consider the other acids as also derivable from water by substitution of oxygen by the acid radicals S, $SO_3$, $SO_4$, $CO_3$, and $C_2O_4$.

## SUGGESTED READING

Alsobrook, J. W. "Jean Baptiste André Dumas," *Journal of Chemical Education,* **28,** 630 (1951).

de Milt, C. "Auguste Laurent, Founder of Modern Organic Chemistry," *Chymia,* **4,** 85 (1953); "Auguste Laurent, Guide and Inspiration of Gerhardt," *Journal of Chemical Education,* **28,** 198 (1951).

Findlay, A. *A Hundred Years of Chemistry,* Chapter 2. New York: The Macmillan Company, 1937.

Leicester, H. M. "Dumas, Davy and Liebig," *Journal of Chemical Education,* **28,** 352 (1951).

Wheland, G. W. "The Early History of Aliphatic Chlorination," in *Advanced Organic Chemistry,* 3rd ed. New York: John Wiley and Sons, 1960, pp. 758–761.

# CHAPTER 6

# A "Crucial Experiment" and

# Gerhardt's Four Types

The contrasting views of Laurent and Liebig were put, as we shall see, to an elegant test by Alexander William Williamson,[1] Professor of Chemistry at London University, and by G. Chancel, working independently, both of whom had met Laurent during their researches in Paris.

## A. W. WILLIAMSON — FROM ALCOHOL TO ETHER

Williamson's paper on the constitution of ether appeared in 1850, four years after Laurent's. It describes what may accurately be termed a crucial experiment, since it tells how he arrived at a decision as to the formulas for alcohol and ether. Hoping to make higher alcohols, he devised a method for substituting ethyl for hydrogen in ethyl alcohol; however, he obtained ether instead. He had carried out his experiment according to the ideas expressed in the substitution theory, replacing hydrogen by potassium and the latter by

[1] Alexander William Williamson (1824–1904): Professor of Chemistry in London and a student of Liebig. He lost an arm and the use of one eye as a child. Williamson prepared ketones by the distillation of calcium salts of organic acids and made early suggestions as to the mechanisms of organic reactions.

ethyl from ethyl iodide. The formation of ether suggests that it contained two ethyl radicals, one coming from the alcohol and the other from the iodide. WILLIAMSON wrote as follows:

▼ "When sulphuric acid is brought in contact with alcohol under certain circumstances, a new arrangement is effected in the elements of the alcohol, which divide into two groups forming ether and water. Now it is well known that the process by which this change is effected may be represented in two ways, the difference of which consists in their respectively selecting for starting point a different view of the constitution of alcohol. According to the one view, an atom [molecule] of alcohol weighs 23 [C = 6, H = ½, O = 8] and is made up of $C^2H^6O$; so that to form ether, two atoms of it are needed, one of which takes $C^2H^4$ from the other, setting free the water with which these elements were combined; whereas according to the other view, alcohol weighs 46 and *contains* ether and water [$C_4H_{10}O.H_2O$]. . . . If by any direct fact we could decide which of these two expressions is the correct one, the ground would be clear for an examination of the process of etherification itself. . . .

"My object in commencing the experiments was to obtain new alcohols, by substituting carburetted hydrogen [a hydrocarbon radical] for hydrogen in a known alcohol. With this view I had recourse to an expedient, which may render valuable services on similar occasions.

"It consisted in replacing the hydrogen first by potassium, and acting upon the compound thus formed by the chloride or iodide of the carburetted hydrogen which was to be introduced in the place of that hydrogen. I commenced with common alcohol, which after careful purification, was saturated with potassium, and as soon as the action had ceased, mixed with a portion of iodide of ethyl equivalent to the potassium used. Iodide of potassium was readily formed on the application of a gentle heat, and the desired substitution was effected; but to my astonishment, the compound thus formed had none of the properties of an alcohol — it was nothing else than common ether $C^4H^{10}O$.

"Now this result at once struck me as being inconsistent with the higher formula of alcohol; for if that body contained twice as many atoms of oxygen as are in ether, I ought clearly to have obtained a product containing twice as much oxygen as ether does."[2]                                                     ▲

2 A. W. WILLIAMSON, *The London, Edinburgh and Dublin Philosophical Magazine and Journal of Science*, [3], **37**, 350 (1850), reprinted in A. W. Williamson, *Papers on Etherification and on the Constitution of Salts*, Alembic Club Reprint, No. 16 (Edinburgh: E. and S. Livingstone, Ltd., 1949), pp. 7–8. The paper was reprinted with a change in style in *Quarterly Journal of the Chemical Society*, **4**, 106 (1852); cf. O. T. Benfey, *Journal of Chemical Education*, **36**, 571 (1959).

In other words, if alcohol were $C_4H_{10}O.H_2O$, i.e. $C_4H_{12}O_2$, the potassium salt would be $C_4H_{10}O_2K_2$, and its reaction with ethyl iodide, liberating potassium iodide, would leave the two atoms of oxygen in the ether. WILLIAMSON continues:

▼ "The alternative was evident, for having obtained ether by substituting $C^2H^5$ for H in alcohol, . . . alcohol is $\begin{matrix} C^2H^5 \\ H \end{matrix} O$, and the potassium compound is $\begin{matrix} C^2H^5 \\ K \end{matrix} O$; and by acting upon this by iodide of ethyl we have

$$\begin{matrix} C^2H^5 \\ K \end{matrix} O + C^2H^5I = IK + \begin{matrix} C^2H^5 \\ C^2H^5 \end{matrix} O$$

. . . Alcohol is therefore water in which half the hydrogen is replaced by carburetted hydrogen, and ether is water in which both atoms of hydrogen are replaced by carburetted hydrogen, thus:

$$\begin{matrix} H \\ H \end{matrix} O \qquad \begin{matrix} C^2H^5 \\ H \end{matrix} O \qquad \begin{matrix} C^2H^5 \\ C^2H^5 \end{matrix} O$$

This formation of ether might, however, be explained, after a fashion, by the other theory—by supposing the potassium compound to contain ether and potash, which separate during the action of the iodide of ethyl; so that half the ether obtained would have been contained in that compound, and the other half formed by double decomposition between potash and iodide of ethyl, thus:

$$\begin{matrix} C^4H^{10}O \\ K^2O \end{matrix} + C^4H^{10}I^2 = 2IK + 2(C^4H^{10}O)$$

But although the insufficiency of this explanation becomes evident on a little reflection, I devised a further and more tangible method of arriving at a conclusion. It consisted in acting upon the potassium compound by iodide of methyl in which case I should, if that compound were ether and potash, obtain a mixture of ether and oxide of methyl [diethyl and dimethyl ether] whereas in the contrary case I should obtain a body of the composition $C^3H^8O$. Now this substance I obtained, and neither ether nor oxide of methyl.

"In this experiment the two theories cross one another, and must lead to different results. . . ."[3] ▲

[3] A. W. WILLIAMSON, Alembic Club Reprint, No. 16, pp. 8–10.

Williamson does not give equations, but we can surmise that for the two possible cases they would be as follows:

(a) Liebig formulas:

$$C^4H^{10}O$$
$$+ C^2H^6I^2 = 2IK + C^4H^{10}O + C^2H^6O$$
$$K_2O \qquad\qquad\qquad \text{"ether"} \qquad \text{"oxide of}$$
$$\text{(diethyl} \qquad \text{methyl"}$$
$$\text{ether)} \qquad \text{(dimethyl ether)}$$

(b) Water-type formulas:

$$C^2H^5 \qquad\qquad\qquad\qquad C^2H^5$$
$$O + CH^3I = IK + \qquad\qquad O$$
$$K \qquad\qquad\qquad\qquad\qquad CH^3$$
$$\text{methyl ethyl}$$
$$\text{ether}$$

WILLIAMSON goes on to state:

▼ ". . . It is clear that if alcohol contain ether and water, and the carburetted hydrogen in my first experiment formed a second atom of ether by taking the place of the hydrogen of this water, that the process being the same in the second experiment, we should then have obtained two ethers. Whereas if the formation of ether from alcohol be effected by synthesis, a new carburetted hydrogen being added to the one already contained in the alcohol, we ought to obtain the new intermediate ether which I obtained.

"The complete description of this remarkable body and of its decompositions, will form the subject of a future paper. I will now merely state that its boiling point is a little above 10° Cent.; it is possessed of a very peculiar smell, distinctly different from that of common ether; and, like that body, it is only slightly soluble in water. It is not acted upon by the alkali metals at the common atmospheric temperature."[4]    ▲

Williamson then proceeds to describe the preparation of ethyl amyl ether [$C_2H_5OC_5H_{11}$] by an analogous procedure. He also demonstrates that methyl ethyl ether can be prepared from $C_2H_5OK$ and $CH_3I$ and from $CH_3OK$ and $C_2H_5I$. This finding must imply that the oxygen atom is not attached more firmly to one radical than to another: $C_2H_5O.CH_3$ is identical with $CH_3O.C_2H_5$.

## EXTENSION TO ACIDS

Two years later WILLIAMSON published detailed properties of the new mixed ethers and extended the applicability of the *water type* to organic acids:

[4] *Ibid.*, p. 10.

▼ "I must beg leave to direct your attention for a moment to the relation between alcohol and acetic acid . . . . You are aware that this acid is essentially monobasic [because it only forms one sodium salt] in its characters like the other terms of the series to which it belongs, and that, in conjunction with other reasons, this circumstance has been urged by M. Gerhardt as ground for halving its formula [from $C_4H_8O_4$, see page 10]. Now as acetic acid is formed from alcohol by replacing one-third of its hydrogen by oxygen, there are strong grounds for assuming a similar constitution in both, and of writing acetic acid at half its usual atomic weight, in accordance with the reduced formula of alcohol. Viewing, therefore, alcohol as water in which half the hydrogen is replaced by ethyl $C_2H_5$ , we

$$\begin{matrix} & O \\ H & \end{matrix}$$

shall consider acetic acid as containing one equivalent of oxygen in the place of two atoms of hydrogen of that radical, or $C_2H_3O$ . Organic

$$\begin{matrix} & O \\ H & \end{matrix}$$

chemistry is replete with instances of differences similar to those between alcohol and acetic acid, and produced by the substitution of an electronegative element for hydrogen. . . ."[5]                                                   ▲

The above formula for acetic acid permitted the inclusion of esters, the pleasant smelling constituents of fruits, in the water type. By replacement of H by $C_2H_5$ in acetic acid, ethyl acetate $C_2H_3O$ is obtained in complete analogy

$$\begin{matrix} O \\ C_2H_5 \end{matrix}$$

with Williamson's ether synthesis from alcohol. Williamson further predicted the possibility of replacing the H of acetic acid by a second $C_2H_3O$ group forming $C_2H_3O$ which, if a molecule of water were added, should form two

$$\begin{matrix} O \\ C_2H_3O \end{matrix}$$

molecules of acetic acid. It therefore represented acetic anhydride, the acid anhydride of acetic acid, long sought by chemists by analogy with the inorganic anhydrides $SO_2$ and $P_2O_5$, whose aqueous solutions contain the acids $H_2SO_3$ and $H_3PO_4$. In fact, as pointed out earlier, the addition of water was considered not to cause any significant chemical change, and acids were commonly represented in their anhydrous form.

## IN SEARCH OF ACETIC ANHYDRIDE

One group of organic acid anhydrides had been discovered earlier, the anhydrides of dibasic acids. These acids, distinguished by the fact that they

---

[5] A. W. WILLIAMSON, *Quarterly Journal of the Chemical Society,* **4,** 229 (1852); Alembic Club Reprint, No. 16, p. 36.

formed both a mono- and disodium salt, and often a mixed salt containing both sodium and potassium in the same substance, were easily dehydrated by heating. Thus succinic acid, $C_4H_6O_4$, was neutralized by sodium hydroxide to form first $C_4H_5O_4Na$ and then $C_4H_4O_4Na_2$. It can also form $C_4H_4O_4NaK$. On heating, it loses a molecule of water, yielding succinic anhydride:

$$C_4H_6O_4 \xrightarrow{heat} C_4H_4O_3 + H_2O$$

But under the same conditions, acetic and benzoic acids decompose completely. This was difficult to reconcile with the dualistic viewpoint according to which acids were supposed to "contain" water as Williamson put it.

In 1852, Charles Gerhardt finally succeeded in preparing acetic and other anhydrides by following exactly the procedure outlined by Williamson.[6] He reacted acetyl chloride with potassium acetate according to the equation

$$\begin{matrix} C_2H_3O \\ O + C_2H_3OCl \rightarrow KCl + \\ K \end{matrix} \quad \begin{matrix} C_2H_3O \\ O \\ C_2H_3O \end{matrix}$$

whereas Williamson's equation for the formation of ether had been

$$\begin{matrix} C_2H_5 \\ O + C_2H_5I \rightarrow KI + \\ K \end{matrix} \quad \begin{matrix} C_2H_5 \\ O \\ C_2H_5 \end{matrix}$$

The reactions are clearly of the same form, and the predictive power of the new concepts was established.

Through these researches, alcohols, ethers, acids, esters, and anhydrides had all been relegated to one inorganic type, that of water $\begin{matrix} H \\ H \end{matrix} O$, from which they are derived by substitution of hydrogen atoms by organic radicals. It was not long before chemists began to seek analogous organizing patterns in compounds not containing oxygen. In fact another "type" in the new sense, that is, a simple inorganic formula from which organic substances are considered as derived by substitution, was set up in 1849 by C. A. Wurtz[7] and A. W. Hofmann.[8]

[6] C. F. Gerhardt, *Annales de Chimie et de Physique,* **37,** 285 (1853).

[7] Charles Adolphe Wurtz (1817–1884): Professor of Organic Chemistry in Paris. He was a pupil of Dumas and Liebig; Couper, van't Hoff, and le Bel studied in his laboratory. Wurtz investigated phosphorus and nitrogen compounds, discovered the "Wurtz reaction" of alkyl halides with sodium to form alkanes, and established the formulas for glycerol and glycol.

[8] A. W. Hofmann (1818–1892): One of Liebig's students who was for twenty years Professor of Chemistry in London (1845–1864); he later founded the German Chemical Society.

## TYPE NUMBER TWO — AMMONIA

Wurtz, a pupil of Dumas and an associate of Laurent and Gerhardt, had prepared methylamine and ethylamine from substituted cyanic acids and from substituted ureas.[9] His products were similar to ammonia both in chemical properties and formulas which he represented in the following two ways (C = 6, H = 1, Az is nitrogen, N):

---

▼ $H^3Az$, ammoniaque ............    $AzH^2,H$, hydramide

$C^2H^5Az$, methylammoniaque .....    $AzH^2,C^2H^3$, methylamide

$C^4H^7Az$, ethylammoniaque ......    $AzH^2,C^4H^5$, ethylamide    ▲

---

If converted to present atomic weights and symbols, the second series would read $HNH_2$, $CH_3NH_2$, $C_2H_5NH_2$.

For a long time, organic bases had been of interest to chemists because they included the class of compounds known as alkaloids ("alkali-like"), among them quinine, strychnine, morphine, and codeine. These substances, extracted from plants, had exhibited powerful physiological effects. They were of interest theoretically because organic nitrogen compounds, being basic, seemed to correspond to the inorganic metallic oxides. *Organic* oxides (ethers), on the other hand, were neutral. Ammonia, as WURTZ had stated in his paper on the amines, belongs with the organic bases:

---

▼     "Certainly ammonia should be regarded as the simplest and most powerful organic base. For all chemists it should represent the type of that large class of bodies, if it were not for one characteristic, important no doubt, but to which perhaps an exaggerated importance has been attributed. Ammonia does not contain carbon."[10]    ▲

---

The syntheses of Wurtz were not simple enough to demonstrate clearly the substitution of hydrogen by methyl or ethyl. This was achieved by Hofmann, who treated ammonia with ethyl iodide and obtained mono-, di-, and triethylated ammonia as well as tetraethylammonium iodide (corresponding to inorganic ammonium iodide, $NH_4I$). They were represented by HOFMANN (modified to conform to C = 12 instead of C = 6) as shown at the top of page 57.[11]

---

[9] C. A. WURTZ, *Comptes rendus de l'Académie des Sciences,* **28,** 223 (1849); cf. *Source Book,* p. 362.

[10] *Ibid.*

[11] A. W. HOFMANN, *Quarterly Journal of the Chemical Society,* **3,** 281 (1851); cf. *Source Book,* p. 364.

$\left.\begin{array}{l} H \\ H \\ H \end{array}\right\}$ N ammonia   $\left.\begin{array}{l} H \\ H \\ C_2H_5 \end{array}\right\}$ N ethylamine

$\left.\begin{array}{l} H \\ C_2H_5 \\ C_2H_5 \end{array}\right\}$ N diethylamine   $\left.\begin{array}{l} C_2H_5 \\ C_2H_5 \\ C_2H_5 \end{array}\right\}$ N triethylamine

$\left.\begin{array}{l} H \\ H \\ H \\ H \end{array}\right\}$ NI ammonium iodide   $\left.\begin{array}{l} C_2H_5 \\ C_2H_5 \\ C_2H_5 \\ C_2H_5 \end{array}\right\}$ NI tetraethylammonium iodide

## GERHARDT'S TYPE QUARTET

To the water and ammonia types Gerhardt now added two others: (*a*) that of hydrogen, $H_2$, which when substituted leads to the series of hydrocarbons, and (*b*) that of hydrogen chloride, HCl, to include the chlorine derivatives of hydrocarbons such as methyl and ethyl chloride.

To these four types, $H_2$, HCl, $H_2O$, and $NH_3$, was added the methane type, $CH_4$, by Kekulé in 1857. This seemingly innocuous proposal, as we shall see, turned out to be the necessary step for the elucidation of the atomic arrangement in organic compounds.

Before we reach this stage, however, a number of other developments have to be considered.

## THE ORDERLY PROGRESSION OF RADICALS

Although the type theory provided a way to classify organic *compounds*, it furnished no clue as to the classification of the radicals. *Any* hydrocarbon radical substituted for one hydrogen atom in water will form an alcohol. When the new principles for determining atomic and molecular weights were used, however, and the formulas of the radicals were examined, they fell into an ordered series, termed "homologous series," such as the following:

| | | | |
|---|---|---|---|
| $CH_3$ | methyl | CHO | formyl |
| $C_2H_5$ | ethyl | $C_2H_3O$ | acetyl |
| $C_3H_7$ | propyl | $C_3H_5O$ | propionyl |
| $C_4H_9$ | butyl | $C_4H_7O$ | butyryl |
| $C_5H_{11}$ | amyl | | |

The difference between succeeding members usually was a $CH_2$ group, though occasionally a multiple of $CH_2$ was found. The existence of such a series was becoming more probable throughout this period as chemists began working on comparative studies using a number of different radicals in the same class of compounds (cf. Williamson's work on ethers).

The principles of classification were defined as follows: (a) according to fundamental and derived nuclei (Laurent), (b) according to types, and (c) according to homologous series. This classification became the basis for two large compilations of organic compounds: Leopold Gmelin's *Handbuch der Anorganischen Chemie* and Friedrich Beilstein's *Handbuch der Organischen Chemie*. The latter covers the entire organic chemical literature, but owing to the accelerating rate at which research is published, it cannot keep abreast of current developments. The original series of volumes reported on all data up to 1909. The first and second supplements cover work up to 1919 and 1929, respectively, whereas the present series attempts to report on the period from 1929 to 1946.

## ORGANIC RESIDUES

Gerhardt tried to reject radicals along with the dualistic theory, feeling certain that they were not analogous to elements. However, in developing his type theory, he found himself forced to use atomic groupings often identical with the radicals. He made clear that these groupings were arbitrarily chosen for the convenience of the chemist when expressing chemical reactions. He called these groups *residues* for the following reason: Substitution reactions involve the removal of an atom or group from a molecule and the introduction of another. But the entering group is almost always part of a larger molecule; the part that is left combines with the ejected group. Thus

$$Cl_2 + CH_3CO_2H \rightarrow CH_2ClCO_2H + HCl$$

chlorine    acetic acid         chloracetic    hydrogen
                                    acid         chloride

Here the reaction involves the elimination of hydrogen chloride from the pair of reagents, while the *residues* Cl and $CH_2CO_2H$ combine. Gerhardt attempted, sometimes with considerable ingenuity, to force every chemical reaction into such a mold of "double decomposition." Another example, where one residue is also a hydrocarbon radical, occurs in the nitration of benzene

$$C_6H_5H + HO.NO_2 \rightarrow H_2O + C_6H_5NO_2$$

benzene    nitric acid    water    nitrobenzene

The residues $C_6H_5$ and $NO_2$ combine when the water is eliminated. This scheme was later attacked by Couper (cf. page 93) since it purported to be a single pattern for all chemical reactions and thus tended to discourage further inquiry.

## THE DISMEMBERMENT OF RADICALS AND RESIDUES

Gerhardt's disbelief in the reality of radicals permitted him and his followers to dissect organic formulas in different ways according to the characteristics they tried to emphasize. And even among the supporters of radicals there was a move to demonstrate the complex nature of some of them. Whereas the radical of acetic acid was usually represented satisfactorily by the formula $C_2H_3$ (using modern atomic weights), so that the acetyl group was $C_2H_3O$, Hermann Kolbe[12] and Edward Frankland (see page 62) showed in 1848 that acetic acid could be obtained by treating methyl cyanide ($CH_3CN$) with dilute acids or bases.[13] It was therefore concluded that acetic acid must contain a methyl group, and that the acetic acid radical was complex and should be written as $CH_3.C$. The acetyl group then becomes $CH_3.CO$ and, when introduced into the water type, acetic acid can be represented as

$$\left. \begin{array}{l} CH_3.CO \\ \\ H \end{array} \right\} O$$

, a formula almost identical with that used today. However, Gerhardt considered the mode of attachment of the atoms in the acetyl group to be an insoluble problem.

### ENTER MULTIPLE TYPES

The use of Gerhardt's four simple types, $H_2$, $HCl$, $H_2O$, and $NH_3$, left many highly complex residues unresolved. Their resolution by Kolbe and others called for an expansion of the type system. Williamson in his papers on ether published in 1852 had proposed that a multiple water type should be employed for polybasic acids when a single water type is too clumsy or misleading. Sulfuric acid, $H_2SO_4$, when represented as

$$\left. \begin{array}{l} HSO_3 \\ \\ H \end{array} \right\} O$$

, suggests a difference between the two hydrogens which is not actually observed. Both hydrogens, for instance, are replaceable by sodium. Williamson suggested for the acid a double water type,

$$\left. \begin{array}{l} H_2 \\ \\ H_2 \end{array} \right\} O_2$$

, with one of the $H_2$ groups replaced by $SO_2$. Sulfuric acid thus becomes

$$\left. \begin{array}{l} SO_2 \\ \\ H_2 \end{array} \right\} O_2$$

and the two hydrogens are equivalent. The validity of the double water type was later made clearer by writing

---

[12] Hermann Kolbe (1818–1884): Professor of Chemistry at Marburg and Leipzig, Germany. He carried out numerous organic chemical researches and made significant theoretical contributions, particularly in the study of organic radicals and their significance in the construction of molecules.

[13] H. Kolbe and E. Frankland, *Annalen der Chemie und Pharmacie,* **65,** 288 (1848).

the two water molecules adjacent to each other and replacing the two hydrogens by one $SO_2$ group:

$$\left.\begin{array}{c}H\\H\end{array}\right\}O \qquad \left.\begin{array}{c}H\\SO_2\end{array}\right\}O$$

$$\left.\begin{array}{c}H\\H\end{array}\right\}O \qquad \left.\begin{array}{c}H\end{array}\right\}O$$

Thus multiple types were held together by atoms or groups that were capable of replacing more than one atom of hydrogen.

The idea of an atom or group "holding together" other atoms or groups is the germ of the idea of "valence" or combining power. WILLIAMSON first used it in discussing a reaction in which two molecules of potassium hydroxide (KOH) form one of potassium carbonate ($K_2CO_3$):

---

▼    "1 atom of carbonic oxide [CO] is here equivalent to 2 atoms of hydrogen, and by replacing them, holds together the two atoms of hydrate in which they were contained, thus necessarily forming a bibasic compound

$$\left.\begin{array}{c}(CO)\\K_2\end{array}\right\}O_2 \quad .^{14}$$

▲

---

Later the same formula would be represented by

$$\left.\begin{array}{c}K\\CO\\K\end{array}\right.\begin{array}{c}\}O\\\}O\end{array}$$

At this stage of development it was a simple step for Odling, Kekulé, and others to propose that multiple types need not contain only one kind of Gerhardt's types but could be composed of several. A water type could be "condensed" with a hydrogen type through a CO group

$$\left.\begin{array}{c}H\\H\end{array}\right\} \qquad \left.\begin{array}{c}H\\CO\end{array}\right\}$$

$$\left.\begin{array}{c}H\\H\end{array}\right\}O \qquad \left.\begin{array}{c}H\end{array}\right\}O$$

---

[14] A. W. WILLIAMSON, *Chemical Gazette*, **9**, 334 (1851), reprinted in *Papers on Etherification and on the Constitution of Salts*, Alembic Club Reprint, No. 16, p. 46, and in *Classics*, p. 73.

to give formic acid ($HCO_2H$), while a further introduction of a methyl group leads to acetic acid

$$CH_3 \atop CO \atop H \Big\} O$$

The rules for the combination of types were spelled out clearly by KEKULÉ in 1857:

▼    "A *monatomic* radical can never keep together two molecules of the types.

"A diatomic radical can unite two molecules of the types.

"A triatomic radical unites in the same way three molecules of the types."[15]    ▲

But to arrive at this clarification, one other major contribution was necessary — the elucidation of the meaning of atomicity or valence which was to make possible the application of Kekulé's rules.

[15] F. A. KEKULÉ, *Annalen der Chemie und Pharmacie*, **104**, 129 (1857); trans. in C. Schorlemmer, *The Rise and Development of Organic Chemistry*, p. 71.

## SUGGESTED READING

Riegel, E. R. "Four Eminent Chemists Who Died before Their Time," *Journal of Chemical Education*, **3**, 1105 (1926).

Wall, F. E. "Faraday, Hofmann and Wurtz," *Journal of Chemical Education*, **28**, 355 (1951).

Williamson, A. W. *Papers on Etherification and the Constitution of Salts*, Alembic Club Reprint, No. 16. Edinburgh: E. and S. Livingstone, 1949.

Winderlich, R. "History of the Chemical Sign Language," *Journal of Chemical Education*, **30**, 58 (1953).

# CHAPTER 7

# Edward Frankland and the
# Enunciation of the
# Valence Concept

In Chapter 6 we read how chemists attempted to apply Gerhardt's four types to some complex molecules and found that, by combining two molecules of the same or different types, complex molecules could be accounted for. But in order to join two "type molecules" some atom or group had to have the capacity of forming more than one attachment. Williamson suggested that the carbonyl group, CO, had this property, but no rule was available for finding other similar groups. Chemists were not even aware of the fact that there was a limit to the number of attachments available to a given atom. The idea of a limited combining capacity originated with Edward Frankland.[1] He had studied with Liebig and Bunsen and for a time collaborated with Hermann Kolbe (see page 59). It was Kolbe who had aroused his interest in the production of free hydrocarbon radicals.

## CAN RADICALS BE LIBERATED?

Robert Bunsen, as we have seen (cf. page 36), had claimed the preparation of the free cacodyl radical, $(CH_3)_2As$, from cacodyl chloride and zinc,

[1] Edward Frankland (1825–1899): Professor of Chemistry in Manchester and London. He carried out studies on carboxylic acids, nitriles, and organometallic compounds. With Lockyer he discovered helium in the sun.

but, as demonstrated much later, he had actually isolated a compound of twice the molecular weight, $((CH_3)_2As)_2$.

Bunsen had pointed out in his article that the production of cacodyl from cacodyl chloride and zinc suggested that a similar attack by a metal on chlorides of hydrocarbons should lead to the production of free hydrocarbon radicals, e.g.

$$C_2H_5Cl + Ag \rightarrow C_2H_5 + AgCl$$

Such hydrocarbon radicals had been earlier claimed by Kolbe as the products of the electrolysis of sodium salts of acetic and similar acids.[2]

$$2CH_3CO_2Na + 2H_2O \xrightarrow[\text{current}]{\text{electric}} 2CH_3 + 2CO_2 + 2NaOH + H_2$$

sodium acetate                    "free methyl"
                          (actually ethane, $C_2H_6$)

Bunsen had, in fact, attempted to make hydrocarbon radicals by his proposed procedure, but had failed, attributing his failure to the low boiling points of the chlorides that he used. He concluded that the reason why he was successful with cacodyl was that the boiling point of cacodyl chloride was higher than 90°C., the temperature at which the reaction with zinc commenced. He therefore proposed that "it will be of great interest to subject organic halides under the pressure of their own vapors, at higher temperatures, to the influence of metals." It was, of course, generally known that the speed of a reaction normally increased markedly as the temperature of the reaction mixture was raised. If open vessels were used, the available temperature range was limited by the boiling points of the reagents. By carefully sealing reagents in glass tubes, the temperature could be increased considerably (if the tube did not explode), and the inability of the vapors to expand led to a great increase of pressure in the container. This often speeded the reaction further.

The idea of producing "free" radicals by an attack of metals on organic halides was logical on the basis of experience with inorganic compounds. It was well known that metals varied in reactivity; therefore one could set up a "reactivity series" with the most reactive, such as sodium and potassium, at one end and the least reactive, such as the noble metals silver, gold, and platinum, at the other. It was a property of this series that a more reactive metal, when added to an aqueous solution of a salt of a less reactive metal, would displace that metal and precipitate it, thus

$$Zn + CuCl_2 \rightarrow ZnCl_2 + Cu \downarrow$$

zinc    copper        zinc      copper
        chloride    chloride

[2] H. Kolbe, *Annalen der Chemie und Pharmacie*, **65**, 288 (1848).

If hydrocarbon radicals were organic equivalents of metals, they should fit somewhere in this series. "Methyl" and "ethyl" should be capable of isolation from their chlorides.

But Bunsen never attempted the high temperature reaction he proposed; his attention was diverted to physical chemistry.

## EDWARD FRANKLAND — FREE RADICALS, ALMOST

Now Frankland took up the problem of preparing hydrocarbon radicals from alkyl halides. As a by-product of what he erroneously considered the successful isolation of free "ethyl," he discovered, as we shall see, a new organo-metallic compound, zinc ethyl, whose analysis led him to a far-reaching conclusion as to the "combining power" or, as we would say, "valence" of the elements.

▼                  *"On the Isolation of the Organic Radicals*
                        *by E. Frankland*

"Considering the importance of having positive proof of the existence of the hitherto hypothetical radicals entering, on the one hand, into the composition of the basic compounds of which alcohol is a type, and on the other, giving rise to the acids of the series commencing with formic acid, it is somewhat remarkable that so few attempts have been made either to isolate these radicals, or at least to discover the simpler groups into which they are decomposed at the moment of their separation.

"Although the method by which Bunsen succeeded in isolating cacodyl pointed out the conditions under which a similar separation of other radicals might be effected, yet with the exception of an unsuccessful attempt by Löwig to obtain ethyl by the action of potassium upon chloride of ethyl, the subject does not seem to have received further attention until Kolbe succeeded in isolating valyl $C_8H_9$ [now called *butyl*, $C_4H_9$] by an entirely different method, viz., by the electrolysis of valeric acid $[C_4H_9CO_2H]$."[3]                                                          ▲

Frankland decided to use zinc rather than the more reactive potassium and ethyl *iodide* because iodides were known to react more readily than chlorides or bromides. For this first experiment he used finely divided zinc in a special tube designed for the purpose:

▼    "In order to subject this liquid, in contact with different metals, to temperatures considerably above the boiling point, and at the same time to preserve any gases that might be evolved, the following method was

[3] E. FRANKLAND, *Quarterly Journal of the Chemical Society*, **2**, 263 (1850).

adopted: tubes of hard Bohemian glass, 1 cm. in diameter, the thickness of the glass being about 1.8 mm., were cut into lengths of 12 inches each, and carefully closed at one end before the blow-pipe so as not to diminish the thickness of the glass. The metals, either finely granulated, or otherwise treated so as to expose a large surface, were then introduced, and the open extremity of the tube was drawn out to the thickness of a straw; about an inch of this narrow tube, at *b* in Figure 4, was then brought into the hottest portion of the flame and the glass allowed to shrink up until a fine capillary bore was obtained; the narrow tube was then bent twice at right angles as shown in the figure. The whole being now warmed, the open extremity was immersed in the iodide of ethyl, which by the subsequent contraction of the enclosed air, was formed into the apparatus in the required quantity; the tube (*a*) being then connected with an air pump by means of a strong caoutchouc [rubber] joint, the apparatus was exhausted and the tube hermetically sealed at *b*: as the liquid boiled violently during the exhaustion, it was easy to effect the expulsion of the last traces of air. The tubes thus prepared were afterwards exposed to the necessary heat by immersing them to half their length in an oil-bath.

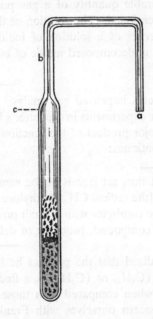

**FIGURE 4**

*Frankland's specially designed reaction tubes which he used when trying to prepare organic radicals. After E. Frankland, Quarterly Journal of the Chemical Society, 2, 263 (1850).*

"A preliminary experiment, conducted as above described, showed that the decomposition of iodide of ethyl, by zinc, commences at a temperature of about 150°C (302°F) [ethyl iodide boils at 72°C.] and proceeds with tolerable rapidity when an extensive surface of the metal is exposed; white crystals gradually encrust the zinc and glass, whilst a colorless mobile liquid remains, equal in volume to only about half the iodide of ethyl employed, and very different from that liquid in appearance; it was further evident from the cessation of ebullition soon after decomposition commenced, that a gas or highly elastic vapor had been generated. Having been maintained at the above temperature for about two hours and the decomposition appearing to be complete, the tube was removed from the bath and allowed to cool. On, afterwards, breaking off its capillary extremity under water, about forty times its volume of gas was evolved, whilst the whole of the mobile fluid, above mentioned, disappeared; the gas had a strong ethereal odor, burnt with a bright flame and was rapidly and completely absorbed by recently boiled absolute alcohol. On cutting off the upper portion of the tube, and introducing distilled water, the white mass of crystals dissolved with brisk effervescence, occasioned by the evolution of a considerable quantity of a gas possessing properties quite similar to those just mentioned. The solution of the crystals thus obtained possesses all the properties of a solution of iodide of zinc and, with the exception of a trace of undecomposed iodide of ethyl, appeared to contain no organic substance."[4]    ▲

Frankland, using Bunsen's improved gas analysis apparatus, analyzed the gases from this and further experiments in the latter's laboratory in Heidelberg. He concluded that the major product of the reaction is the free ethyl radical. However, FRANKLAND continues:

▼ "a portion of the ethyl thus set free is at the same time decomposed into equal volumes of elayl [the radical $CH_2$ of ethylene ($C_2H_4$)] and methyl . . . whilst the iodide of zinc combines with a small proportion of methyl, forming a white crystalline compound, probably of definite constitution."[5]    ▲

Since Frankland soon realized that the product he had thought of as ethyl, $C_2H_5$, was in fact butane ($C_4H_{10}$ or ($C_2H_5)_2$), a finding based on its boiling point and vapor density when compared with those of other known hydrocarbons, we need not concern ourselves with Frankland's presumed mechanism by which the "white crystalline compound, probably of definite constitution" was obtained. The important fact was that he was aware of it and turned aside from the elusive search for "free radicals" to the consideration

[4] *Ibid.*
[5] *Ibid.*

of the new "organo-metallic" compound. We need only to remark here that conclusive evidence for a free radical was not obtained until 1900 when Moses Gomberg (1866–1947) of the University of Michigan accidentally prepared the radical $(C_6H_5)_3C$ from its chloride by reaction with silver:[6]

$$(C_6H_5)_3CCl + Ag \rightarrow (C_6H_5)_3C + AgCl$$

In 1929, F. Paneth and W. Hofeditz finally demonstrated that ethyl radicals, $C_2H_5$, are in fact formed in the reaction as carried out by Frankland,[7]

$$2C_2H_5Cl + Zn \rightarrow 2C_2H_5 + ZnCl_2$$

but that the radicals exist for only a fraction of a second before combining to form butane

$$2C_2H_5 \rightarrow C_4H_{10}$$

or reacting with each other to form ethylene and ethane

$$2C_2H_5 \rightarrow C_2H_4 + C_2H_6$$

## THE STUDY OF ORGANOMETALLIC COMPOUNDS

Frankland's "white crystalline compound, probably of definite constitution" turned out to be the clue by which the theory of combining capacity was firmly established. He examined this and similar products and reported some of their properties and reactions in a paper immediately following the one just quoted. It was entitled "On a New Series of Organic Bodies containing Metals and Phosphorus," and was read by Frankland before a meeting of the Chemical Society in London on November 5, 1849.[8] At the end of the meeting, A. W. Hofmann "exhibited a specimen of the zinc methyl he had obtained from Dr. Frankland and demonstrated its spontaneous inflammability."

The crystalline residue in the ethyl iodide experiment was later shown to be ethyl zinc iodide ($C_2H_5ZnI$) which on dry distillation forms zinc ethyl ($Zn(C_2H_5)_2$) and zinc iodide ($ZnI_2$).

At first Frankland was tempted to believe, in part because of their considerable reactivity, that zinc methyl ($Zn(CH_3)_2$) and zinc ethyl were new free radicals like the presumed arsenic radical, cacodyl, $As(CH_3)_2$. By 1852, however, he had concluded that all of them, including cacodyl, were normal compounds and not radicals. Though involved, his arguments were essentially

[6] M. Gomberg, *Journal of the American Chemical Society,* **22,** 757 (1900).

[7] F. Paneth and W. Hofeditz, *Berichte der Deutschen Chemischen Gesellschaft,* **62,** 1335 (1929).

[8] E. Frankland, *Quarterly Journal of the Chemical Society,* **2,** 297 (1850).

based on the fact that if cacodyl was a radical it would form compounds of three stages of complexity corresponding to the three levels of oxidation of arsenic, since the attachment of methyl radicals to metal atoms was not considered to affect the element's reactivity with other inorganic elements. Now arsenic forms a sulfide, $As_2S_2$ (the corresponding oxide $As_2O_2$ is still unknown), and two oxides, $As_2O_3$ and $As_2O_5$. Cacodyl, on the other hand, in spite of its great reactivity, only shows two stages of compound formation. Hence, Frankland concluded that cacodyl is not a radical but a *compound* of the arsenic sulfide type, which on oxidation yields cacodylic oxide and cacodylic acid corresponding to the tri- and pentoxides of arsenic, respectively. In this light, cacodylic compounds become organic substitution products of inorganic types and zinc ethyl becomes the organic analogue of zinc oxide. A table from Frankland's paper is given below. It is complicated by the fact that Frankland followed Gmelin's rather than Laurent's atomic weight table, so that O = 8 and some other atomic weights (such as Zn) are halved. In the modern sense, Gmelin used *equivalent* rather than atomic weights, replacing, for instance, a single O in a compound by a single Cl, because the symbol O represented that weight of oxygen equivalent to, or replaceable by, one atomic weight of chlorine. This scheme led to a striking similarity in formulas:

| Inorganic Type | Organo-Metallic Derivatives |
|---|---|
| $As\begin{cases}S\\S\end{cases}$ | $As\begin{cases}C_2H_3\\ \quad \text{cacodyl}\\C_2H_3\end{cases}$ |
| $As\begin{cases}O\\O\\O\end{cases}$ | $As\begin{cases}C_2H_3\\C_2H_3 \quad \text{oxide of cacodyl}\\O\end{cases}$ |
| $As\begin{cases}O\\O\\O\\O\\O\end{cases}$ | $As\begin{cases}C_2H_3\\C_2H_3\\O \quad \text{cacodylic acid}\\O\\O\end{cases}$ |
| ZnO | $Zn(C_2H_3)$ zinc methylium |
| $Zn\begin{cases}O\\O\end{cases}$ | $Zn\begin{cases}C_2H_3\\ \quad \text{oxide of zinc methylium}\\O\end{cases}$ |

## SYMMETRY OF CONSTRUCTION AND THE VALENCE CONCEPT

The above analysis led Frankland to realize that there was a definite limit to the number of distinct ways in which an atom can react. The paper then proceeds with his classic passage enunciating the valence concept:

▼    "When the formulae of inorganic chemical compounds are considered, even a superficial observer is struck with the general symmetry of their construction; the compounds of nitrogen, phosphorus, antimony and arsenic especially exhibit the tendency of these elements to form compounds containing three or five equivalents of other elements, and it is in these proportions that their affinities are best satisfied; thus, in the ternal group we have $NO_3$, $NH_3$, $NI_3$, $NS_3$, $PO_3$, $PH_3$, $PCl_3$, $SbO_3$, $SbH_3$, $SbCl_3$, $AsO_3$, $AsH_3$, $AsCl_3$, &c., and in the five atom group $NO_5$, $NH_4O$, $NH_4I$, $PO_5$, $PH_4I$, &c. Without offering any hypothesis regarding the cause of this symmetrical grouping of atoms, it is sufficiently evident, from the examples just given, that such a tendency or law prevails, and that, *no matter what the character of the uniting atoms may be, the combining power of the attracting element,* if I may be allowed the term, *is always satisfied by the same number of these atoms.*[9]  It was probably a glimpse of the operation of this law amongst the more complex organic groups which led Laurent and Dumas to the enunciation of the theory of types; and had not those distinguished chemists extended their views beyond the point to which they were well supported by then existing facts, had they not assumed that the properties of an organic compound are dependent upon the position, and not upon the nature of its single atoms, that theory would undoubtedly have contributed to the development of the science to a still greater extent than it has already done. Such an assumption could only have been made at a time when the data upon which it was founded were few and imperfect, and as the study of the phenomena of substitution progressed it gradually became untenable, and the fundamental principles of the electro-chemical theory again assumed their sway. The formation and examination of the organo-metallic bodies promise to assist in effecting a fusion of the two theories which have so long divided the opinions of chemists, and which have too hastily been conceived irreconcileable; for whilst it is evident that certain types of series of compounds exist, it is equally clear that the nature of the body derived from the original type is essentially dependent upon the electro-chemical character of its single atoms, and not merely upon the relative position of those atoms."[10]                    ▲

---

[9] Italics added.
[10] E. FRANKLAND, *Philosophical Transactions of the Royal Society of London,* **142,** 417 (1852), reprinted in *Classics,* pp. 104–106.

The key phrase in the above passage "no matter what the character of the uniting atoms may be, the combining power of the attracting element is always satisfied by the same number of these atoms" provided the general conception which was later termed "valence." In this paper Frankland recognized the possibility of multiple combining capacities for atoms such as nitrogen, phosphorus, arsenic, and antimony, all of them showing predominant valences of 3 and 5. Kekulé (cf. Chapter 8), who later claimed priority for the valence concept because Frankland's was based on equivalents, asserted, on the contrary, that the valence was as fixed a property of an element as the atomic weight. To him the pentavalent compounds such as $NH_4I$ and $PCl_5$ were in reality molecular complexes $NH_3.HI$ and $PCl_3.Cl_2$, held together by much weaker forces, and with only three atoms directly attached to nitrogen and phosphorus. Owing to his authority, Kekulé's view prevailed for decades and the associated nomenclature in which, for instance, the methyl derivative of ammonium chloride is called "methylamine hydrochloride" is still often used today.

Thus organic chemists were faced with a new task, namely, to determine the atomicity or combining capacity of the elements. With this knowledge, formulas could then be written with more certainty and chemical behavior predicted with more accuracy.

### SUGGESTED READING

Findlay, A. *A Hundred Years of Chemistry*, Chapter 2. New York: The Macmillan Company, 1937.

Mackle, H. "The Evolution of Valence Theory and Bond Symbolism," *Journal of Chemical Education*, **31**, 618 (1954).

**CHAPTER 8**

# The Tetravalence of Carbon:
# Odling and Kekulé

In most cases the inspection of an element's simple compounds was sufficient for the determination of that element's combining capacity. By this procedure Frankland had deduced the combining capacity of nitrogen and phosphorus. The procedure was not of immediate use in the case of organic compounds, because carbon invariably appeared as part of a radical. What was needed was a way of determining the combining capacity of carbon.

## TYPE NUMBER FIVE — METHANE

Carbon's combining capacity was discovered by an extension of Gerhardt's classification according to simple inorganic "types." Gerhardt had used the types, HH, HCl, $H_2O$, $NH_3$, to which it was now proposed to add a fifth, the methane or marsh gas type, $CH_4$. This seemingly obvious suggestion required, at the time, considerable courage and freedom from the shackles of / previous viewpoints. The purpose of these types, it may be remembered, was to provide an inorganic framework from which, by substitution of organic radicals, all organic compounds were derivable. According to this point of view methane belonged to the hydrogen type (HH) by substitution of one hydrogen by methyl ($CH_3H$). It was expressly for the purpose of classifying the hydrocarbons that the hydrogen type was invented. But as long as carbon was viewed as a part of a radical, its own nature and combining capacity remained a mystery.

71

The methane type was first proposed by William Odling[1] in 1855. Odling's paper revealed the extent to which he had freed himself from the restrictions of current theories. He simply proposed that chloroform ($CHCl_3$) is a derivative of methane since it can be prepared from the latter, and that the two compounds are clearly analogous. By contrast, according to the prevailing type theory methane was classified as belonging to the hydrogen type and chloroform to the triple hydrochloric acid type:

$$\left. \begin{array}{c} CH \\ Cl_3 \end{array} \right\} \text{derived from} \qquad \left. \begin{array}{c} H_3 \\ Cl_3 \end{array} \right\}$$

ODLING wrote as follows:

▼    "Adopting the proportional numbers of Gerhardt, we represent the . . . molecules of muriatic acid, water, ammonia, and coal-gas, by $ClH$, $OH^2$, $NH^3$, $CH^4$ respectively. In accordance with certain theoretical notions, these bodies have been formulated as follows:—

H.Cl

H.OH          $H^2.O$
(Laurent)

$H.NH^2$        $H^2.NH$        $H^3.N$
(Kane)          (Wurtz)

$H.CH^3$        $H^2.CH^2$        $H^3.CH$        $H^4.C$
(Liebig)        (Dumas)        (Odling)

Coal-gas may be represented as terhydryde of formyl [$H^3.CH$] analogous to its derivative chloroform or terchloride of formyl [$Cl^3.CH$ or $CHCl_3$]. The two bodies can be prepared in virtue of analogous equations from acetic and chlor-acetic acids [cf. page 44] respectively, and the one can be obtained from the other by direct substitution [$CH_4 + 3Cl_2 \rightarrow CHCl_3 + 3HCl$]."[2]                                                                    ▲

## KEKULÉ AND THE METHANE TYPE

Two years later, Friedrich August Kekulé,[3] unaware of Odling's paper,

[1] William Odling (1829–1921): Faraday's successor as Professor of Chemistry at the Royal Institution, London, and Professor of Chemistry at Oxford. He translated Laurent's *Chemical Method,* whose views he early espoused and defended in England.

[2] W. ODLING, *Proceedings of the Royal Institution of Great Britain,* **2,** 63 (1855); reprinted in R. Anschütz, *August Kekulé* (Berlin: Verlag Chemie, 1929), **I,** p. 667.

[3] Friedrich August Kekulé (1829–1896): Professor of Chemistry at Ghent, Belgium, and Heidelberg and Bonn, Germany. Originally a student of architecture, he turned to chemistry on hearing Liebig's lectures at Giessen.

also came to recognize the importance of a methane type and drew far-reaching conclusions. In his paper published in 1857, he again took up (cf. page 21) the chemistry of the fulminates — explosives seem to have an unending fascination for chemists. His conclusion as to the constitution of mercury fulminate was quite wrong, but the generalization he derived from it was eminently satisfactory. Using Gmelin's equivalent weights (C = 6, O = 8, Hg = 100.3), Kekulé wrote mercury fulminate as $C_2(NO_4)(C_2N)Hg_2$ which on doubling the atomic weights of oxygen, carbon, and mercury becomes $C(NO_2)(CN)Hg$. The molecular formula $HgC_2N_2O_2$ is accepted today, but fulminic acid is now written HONC so that mercury fulminate becomes $Hg(ONC)_2$. Gerhardt had pointed out the explosive properties of nitro groups and had suggested for fulminic acid the formula $C_4N(NO_4)H_2$. Kekulé now added the proposal that the second nitrogen was part of a cyanide group, because chlorine liberated cyanogen chloride. In this paper KEKULÉ consistently wrote $C_2$ where we would write C:

▼    "I accordingly wrote mercury fulminate as

$$C_2(NO_4)(C_2N)Hg_2.$$

"This formula shows at the first glance that mercury fulminate exhibits in its composition the closest analogy with a large number of known compounds, to which for example, chloroform, $C_2$ H Cl Cl Cl belongs. We might regard it as nitrated chloroform in which the chlorine is replaced partly by cyanogen and partly by mercury.

"The following compounds may be referred to the same type:

| $C_2$ | H | H | H | H | marsh gas |
|---|---|---|---|---|---|
| $C_2$ | H | H | H | Cl | methylic chloride etc. |
| $C_2$ | H | Cl | Cl | Cl | chloroform etc. |
| $C_2$ | $(NO_4)$ | Cl | Cl | Cl | chloropicrin |
| $C_2$ | $(NO_4)$ | $(NO_4)$ | Cl | Cl | Marignac's oil |
| $C_2$ | $(NO_4)$ | Br | Br | Br | bromopicrin |
| $C_2$ | H | H | H | $C_2N$ | acetonitrile |
| $C_2$ | Cl | Cl | Cl | $C_2N$ | trichloro-acetonitrile |
| $C_2$ | $(NO_4)$ | Hg | Hg | $C_2N$ | mercury fulminate |
| $C_2$ | $(NO_4)$ | H | H | $C_2N$ | hypothetical fulminic acid |

"In assigning these compounds to the same type, I . . . use the word in the sense in which it was first employed by Dumas on the occasion of his fruitful investigations on the subject of types. I wish essentially to indicate the relations in which the said compounds stand to one another; that the one, under the influence of appropriate agents, can be produced from or transformed into the other."[4]     ▲

KEKULÉ returned to the subject of the constitution of mercury fulminate in the spring of 1858, and repeated the table of compounds belonging to the methane type, but this time added the explanatory note:

▼     "One may consider all these bodies as belonging to a series, to a mechanical type [cf. page 48]; all contain the same number of atoms [atomic groupings] if one views the nitro group and cyanogen as radicals that are analogous to elements; in their individual properties they show great differences, caused by the differences in the dynamic nature of the entering elements. Some of the bodies, namely those containing cyanogen, can be united in a special group whose representative member is acetonitrile [$CH_3CN$; "aceto," because on hydrolysis it yields acetic acid]; however, with as much right as acetonitrile can be considered as methyl cyanide, the remaining bodies in the group can be viewed as cyanogen-containing derivatives of the type $C_2H_4$ [$CH_4$]. While marsh gas [methane] is an indifferent body, chloride of methyl (belonging to the same type) behaves as a chloride of a *monatomic* radical, and chloroform — at least in some reactions — like the chloride of a triatomic radical. The contrast in the chemical nature of chlorine as compared with that of hydrogen is the cause of the difference in behavior, and the number of chlorine atoms determines the basicity of the residual radical."[5]     ▲

## THE TETRAVALENCE OF CARBON

In a footnote to a slightly earlier paper by KEKULÉ (November, 1857) the tetravalence of carbon was stated in complete clarity:

▼     "Carbon is, as may easily be shown, and as I shall explain in detail on a later occasion, tetrabasic or tetratomic: that is, 1 atom of carbon, $C = 12$, is equivalent to 4 atoms of H.

"The simplest compound of C with an element of the first group [i.e. with a monatomic element], with H or Cl for instance, is therefore $CH_4$ and $CCl_4$."[6]     ▲

[4] F. A. KEKULÉ, *Annalen der Chemie und Pharmacie*, **101**, 200 (1857); trans. by F. R. Japp, *Journal of the Chemical Society*, **73**, 97 (1898).

[5] F. A. KEKULÉ, *Annalen der Chemie und Pharmacie*, **105**, 279 (1858).

[6] F. A. KEKULÉ, *Annalen der Chemie und Pharmacie*, **104**, 129 (1857).

So far so good. But it was not immediately clear how a knowledge of the valence of carbon could be applied to the elucidation of most organic compounds in view of the large number of carbon atoms frequently contained in molecules. Some principle was still needed for the solution of the multiple carbon problem.

## SUGGESTED READING

Darmstaedter, L., and Oesper, R. E. "August Kekulé," *Journal of Chemical Education,* **4,** 697 (1927).

Hiebert, E. N. "The Experimental Basis of Kekulé's Valence Theory," *Journal of Chemical Education,* **36,** 320 (1959).

Rosen, S. "William Odling, Faraday's Successor," *Journal of Chemical Education,* **34,** 517 (1957).

# CHAPTER 9

# The Chain-Forming Capacity
# Of Carbon Atoms:
# Kekulé and Couper

If carbon is tetravalent and a hydrocarbon of formula $\left. \begin{array}{l} CH_3 \\ CH_3 \end{array} \right\}$ is known, it is only a small step to the conclusion that the link between the methyl groups must occur through linkage of the carbon atoms. With type formulas it might be represented thus:

$$\overset{C}{\underset{C}{\big[ H \ \ H \ \ H \ \big| \ \ H \ \ H \ \ H \big]}}$$

Perhaps the second carbon can link to a third, the third to a fourth, and so on. This conclusion was not long in coming. In fact it had been in Kekulé's mind since his stay in London (1853–55), where he had become a close friend of Williamson and Odling.

### THE USE OF OPEN DECK BUSES

In a speech at a much later time (1890) KEKULÉ recalled the origin of these ideas:

▼    "During my stay in London I resided for a considerable time in Clapham Road in the neighbourhood of the Common. I frequently, however, spent my evenings with my friend Hugo Müller at Islington, at the opposite end of the metropolis. We talked of many things, but most often of our beloved chemistry. One fine summer evening I was returning by the last bus, 'outside' as usual, through the deserted streets of the city, which are at other times so full of life. I fell into a reverie, and lo, the atoms were gamboling before my eyes! Whenever, hitherto, these diminutive beings had appeared to me, they had always been in motion; but up to that time I had never been able to discern the nature of their motion. Now, however, I saw how, frequently, two smaller atoms united to form a pair; how a larger one embraced the two smaller ones; how still larger ones kept hold of three or even four of the smaller; whilst the whole kept whirling in a giddy dance. I saw how the larger ones formed a chain, dragging the smaller ones after them but only at the ends of the chain. I saw what our past master, Kopp, my highly honored teacher and friend, has depicted with such charm in his 'Molekularwelt'; but I saw it long before him. The cry of the conductor: 'Clapham Road,' awakened me from my dreaming; but I spent a part of the night in putting on paper at least sketches of these dream forms. This was the origin of the 'Structural Theory'. . . .

"As a young instructor in Heidelberg, I put these views on paper and shared them with two of my closer friends. They shook their heads full of misgivings. I decided that one of two things was not quite ripe, either the theory or the time — so I let my manuscript stay in the desk. . . . More than a year later an article by Limpricht provided the occasion for publishing it, though of course in a modified form. The article did not gain materially from this alteration. It would have suited the purpose better had the polemical part not been printed. To my mind, the earlier form was preferable."[1]                                                            ▲

## GOING BACK TO THE ELEMENTS

If the polemical part is omitted, as Kekulé proposes, the systematic portion of his epoch-making paper of 1858 begins with his pointing out that many of the ideas to be presented by no means originated with him, but owe their origin in part to Williamson, Odling, Gerhardt, and Wurtz. He continues:

▼    "I regard it as necessary and in the present state of chemical knowledge as in many cases possible to explain the properties of chemical compounds by going back to the elements themselves which compose these compounds. I no longer regard it as the chief problem of the time, to prove the presence of atomic groups which, on the strength of certain

[1] F. A. KEKULÉ, *Berichte der Deutschen chemischen Gesellschaft*, **23**, 1302 (1890); trans. (first paragraph by F. R. Japp) in O. T. Benfey, *Journal of Chemical Education*, **35**, 21 (1958).

properties, may be regarded as radicals, and in this way to refer compounds to a few types which can hardly have any significance beyond that of mere pattern formulas. On the contrary I hold that we must extend our investigation to the constitution of the radicals themselves; that we must ascertain the relation of the radicals to one another and, from the nature of the elements, deduce both the nature of the radicals and that of their compounds."[2]    ▲

Working in Paris in Wurtz's laboratory, a young Scotsman, ARCHIBALD SCOTT COUPER,[3] had independently reached the identical conclusion:

▼    "I go back to the elements themselves of which I study the mutual affinities. This study is, in my opinion, sufficient for the explanation of all chemical combinates, without it being necessary to revert to unknown principles and to arbitrary generalizations."[4]    ▲

However, we will study Kekulé's paper first because it preceded Couper's by a few weeks. KEKULÉ's paper continues:

▼    "The simplest combinations of the elements among themselves, as they are determined by the unequal basicities [valences] of the atoms, constitute the simplest types. Compounds may be counted as belonging to a given type, as soon as, in the reaction under observation, the compound is attacked from that particular side which shows the characteristic reaction of the type. I consider by the term radical the residue that is not attacked in the particular reaction, whose constitution, therefore, is of no concern for the moment.

"In order to be more comprehensible, it seems suitable to report first the conception that I have of the process that occurs during chemical reactions. It seems to me as if the main cause of the lack of clarity in certain points of view is the one-sided conception held about such chemical changes.

[2] F. A. KEKULÉ, Annalen der Chemie und Pharmacie, **106**, 129 (1858). The complete article is translated in Classics, pp. 109 ff; for above quotation see p. 115.

[3] Archibald Scott Couper (1831–1892): Studied humanities and classical languages in Glasgow and logic and metaphysics in Edinburgh under Sir William Hamilton who was noted for his success in developing critical powers in his students. Around 1855 in Berlin, he began his studies of chemistry, and then moved to Wurtz's laboratory in Paris. He suffered a nervous breakdown in 1859 and carried on no further significant intellectual work.

[4] A. S. COUPER, Comptes rendus de l'Académie des Sciences, **46**, 1157 (1858); trans. by L. Dobbin in On a New Chemical Theory and Researches on Salicylic Acid. Papers by Archibald Scott Couper, Alembic Club Reprint, No. 21 (Edinburgh: E. and S. Livingstone, Ltd., 1953), p. 9; reprinted in Classics, p. 132.

## Chemical Reactions: Combination and Decomposition

"In earlier periods it seemed sufficient to express the end result of a chemical reaction by an equation; more recently a conception, utilized for long in certain classes of compounds, has been applied universally to all chemical reactions. An attempt was made to conceive all reactions as double decompositions [cf. page 58]. Gerhardt's type theory rests, as Gerhardt himself emphasizes, on the assumption of this reaction as the reaction type. I hope it will become clear in what follows, that this conception is not general enough, since it cannot be applied to all reactions, and because even in the cases where it does apply, it does not go far enough in explaining them.

"Chemical transformations may be classified for the moment under the following points of view, according to the processes occurring at the time:

(1) *Direct addition* of two molecules to form one, occurs relatively seldom; however, $NH_3$ adds directly to HCl; $PCl_3$ to $Cl_2$ etc. . . .

(2) *Combination of several molecules accompanied by relocation of a polyatomic radical.* — The formation of sulfuric acid hydrate [$H_2SO_4$] from $SO_3$ and $H_2O$; of Nordhäuser's oil of vitriol [$H_2S_2O_7$] from anhydrous sulfuric acid [$SO_3$] and sulfuric acid hydrate; the production of hydrates of dibasic acids when water reacts with the anhydride, . . . belong here."[5]

▲

KEKULÉ then gives as an example the reaction of succinimide with water to form succinamic acid:

▼

Succinimide $\longrightarrow$ Succinamic acid

$$\left.\begin{array}{c} \overset{\prime\prime}{C_4}H_4O_2 \\[2mm] H \end{array}\right\}N \qquad\qquad \left.\begin{array}{c} H \\[1mm] \overset{\prime\prime}{C_4}H_4O_2 \end{array}\!\!\!\left.\begin{array}{c} H \\ \end{array}\right\}N \right.$$

$$\left.\begin{array}{c} H \\[2mm] H \end{array}\right\}O \qquad\qquad\qquad \left.\begin{array}{c} H \\[1mm] H \end{array}\right\}O$$

▲

On the left-hand side are represented the reacting molecules of succinimide and water, separated by a horizontal line. The two short slanting lines " over the $C_4H_4O_2$ group indicate the divalent or dibasic character of the group. The group therefore can form two links with other atoms. In succinimide,

[5] *Classics*, pp. 115–116.

since nitrogen has a valence of three, two of its valences are used to link the $C_4H_4O_2$ group leaving one for a linkage to hydrogen. The result of the "relocation" of the polyatomic radical is shown in the right-hand formula for succinamic acid. Here the two valences of the $C_4H_4O_2$ group are used to connect the oxygen and nitrogen atoms of the water and ammonia type molecules, respectively. A single molecule is therefore produced from two reagent molecules. A more modern representation for the same reaction might be as follows:

$$
\begin{array}{ccc}
\begin{array}{l}
CH_2\!-\!C\!-\!-\!N\!-\!H \\
\quad\ \ \underset{O}{\|} \quad\ / \\
\qquad\qquad H \\
CH_2\!-\!C + O\!-\!H \\
\quad\ \ \underset{O}{\|}
\end{array}
& \rightarrow &
\begin{array}{l}
CH_2\!-\!C\!-\!N\!-\!H \\
\quad\ \ \underset{O}{\|}\ \ \ H \\
\ \\
CH_2\!-\!C\!-\!O\!-\!H \\
\quad\ \ \underset{O}{\|}
\end{array}
\end{array}
$$

KEKULÉ proceeds:

▼ "The reverse occurs in many decompositions, for instance in the formation of the anhydrides of dibasic acids. . . . In [these] cases the number of molecules changes and therefore also the volume in the case of gaseous bodies."[6]   ▲

Note here Kekulé's use of Avogadro's hypothesis: If equal numbers of gas molecules occupy equal volumes, then a change in the number of molecules during a reaction at constant pressure will immediately show itself in a change in total volume.

▼    "In a far greater number of reactions the number of molecules remains the same (with gases the volume, also). The change can then be considered as if the one molecule has exchanged a portion of its constituent parts for those of another. Among the reactions generally designated:

(3) *Mutual decomposition* or *double exchange,* two essentially different types must be distinguished. First, it is clear, that always equivalent amounts are exchanged, i.e. a *monatomic* against another *monatomic* radical; a diatomic against another diatomic or, on the other hand, against two monatomic radicals, etc. If there is exchange of radicals of equal atomicity, the number of molecules remains unchanged; if, however, a diatomic radical is replaced by two monatomic ones, the previously indivisible molecule is split into two smaller molecules because the cause of the connection is lost. Conversely, two previously separate molecules are sometimes united into an indivisible whole (into a molecule) when a

---

[6] *Ibid.,* p. 117.

diatomic radical takes the place of two that are monatomic. It is unnecessary to furnish examples for such "double exchange". . . .

"Deserving of emphasis is only that the viewing of such reactions as mutual exchange provides an excellent means for the recognition of the basicity of radicals (and of the elements)."[7]

▲

KEKULÉ proceeds to point out one danger of the "mutual exchange" view, namely, that radicals are thought of as leaving a molecule as independent entities, the impression being gained that

▼    ". . . during the exchange, while in a sense in transit, the radicals (and atoms) exist in a free condition.

"The simplest conception, and one applicable to all chemical changes is the following:

"When two molecules react, they first attract each other by virtue of their chemical affinity, and align themselves next to each other. The affinities of the individual atoms then cause atoms which previously belonged to different molecules to come into intimate contact. For that reason, the group that was divided in one direction prior to reaction now falls apart in another direction, thus:

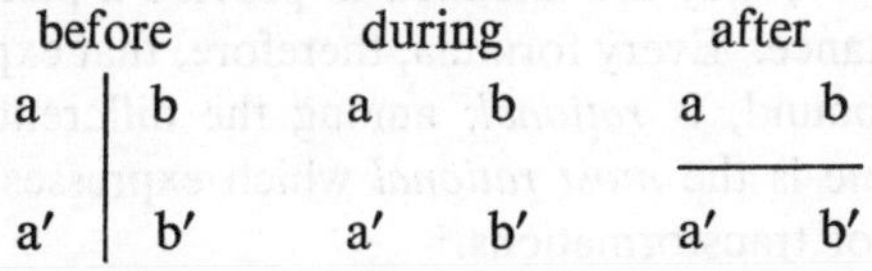

| before | during | after |
|---|---|---|
| a \| b | a    b | a    b |
| a' \| b' | a'   b' | a'   b' |

On comparing product and starting material, the decomposition can be conceived of as a mutual exchange. . . ."[8]

▲

Even very complicated reactions could be viewed as following the new mechanism; for instance, the formation of marsh gas ($CH_4$) from potassium acetate ($CH_3COOK$) and potassium hydroxide ($KOH$) is shown by KEKULÉ as:

▼

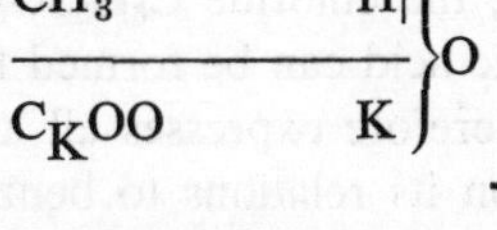

$$CH_3 \qquad H|$$
$$\overline{\phantom{C_KOO \qquad K}} \Big\} O$$
$$C_KOO \qquad K$$

▲

In this form of representation, the reagents potassium acetate and potassium hydroxide appear on the left and right, respectively. The products $CH_4$ and $K_2CO_3$ are separated by the vertical and horizontal lines.

[7] *Ibid.*, pp. 117–118.
[8] *Ibid.*, p. 118.

Similarly the formation of chloroform ($CHCl_3$) from potassium trichloracetate ($CCl_3COOK$) and potassium hydroxide is represented by KEKULÉ as:

▼

$$\left.\begin{array}{cc} CCl_3 & H| \\ \hline C_KOO & K \end{array}\right\}O$$

▲

## THE ANATOMY OF FORMULAS

Having discussed a number of reactions by means of his new representation, Kekulé commences to analyze the purpose and significance of "rational formulas." He is quite certain that we can get no indication as to the location of atoms and groups in a molecule from chemical reactions; all we can learn from them is the manner in which they break up:

▼

√

"Rational formulas are reaction formulas and can be nothing else in the present state of the science. In that their symbolism indicates the atomic groups that remain unattacked in certain reactions (radicals), or emphasize the constituent parts which play a role in certain often recurring transformations (types), they are intended to provide a picture of the chemical nature of a substance. Every formula, therefore, that expresses certain reactions of a compound, is *rational;* among the different rational formulas, however, that one is the *most rational* which expresses simultaneously the largest number of transformations.

Of the three rational formulas of benzene sulfonic acid

$$\left.\begin{array}{c} C_6H_5 \\ \overset{''}{SO_2} \\ H \end{array}\right\}O \qquad \left.\begin{array}{c} C_6H_5SO_2 \\ H \end{array}\right\}O \qquad C_6H_5SO_3,H$$

the first designates (1) that one H atom is easily exchanged for metals, (2) that under the action of $PCl_5$, chlorine takes up the position of the typical O and, in addition to HCl, the chloride $C_6H_5SO_2,Cl$ is formed; it designates (3) that benzene sulfonic acid can be formed from a phenyl [$C_6H_5$] and a sulfuryl compound; it therefore expresses all known reactions of this acid and brings to recollection its relations to benzene and sulfuric acid. The second formula expresses only reactions (1) and (2), while the third finally (hydrogen acid theory) designates only salt formation and takes no account of any other reactions. The first is, therefore, by far the most comprehensive and therefore the most rational. . . .

"In general the most resolved formula will express the nature of a body most completely. If, therefore, we normally prefer a more empirical formula, expressing the most common reactions, we must still admit that the other is more rational. . . ."[9]

▲

If then the most resolved formula expresses the nature of a chemical most completely, the attempt should be made to resolve the radicals themselves into their constituent atoms and to study their mutual interconnections. KEKULÉ addresses himself to this problem in the next section.

▼

### "THE CONSTITUTION OF RADICALS AND THE NATURE OF CARBON

"It has often been pointed out that radicals are not groups of atoms closely bound together but only atoms located near each other, which in certain reactions do not separate, while in others they break apart. It depends on the nature of the atoms which are located together and on the nature of the reacting substance whether or not an atom group plays the part of a so-called "radical" directly, whether it is a more or less stable radical. In general, it can be said that the greater the difference in the nature of the individual atoms, the more easily will an atomic group or a radical break apart.

"It will not be necessary to extend these considerations further; I will give only one example to show how this association of atoms can occur. The radical of sulfuric acid, $SO_2$, contains three atoms, each of which is diatomic, thus representing two affinity units. On joining together, one affinity unit of one atom combines with one of the other. Of the six affinity units, four are thus used to hold the three atoms themselves together; two remain over, and the group appears to be diatomic; it unites, for instance, with two atoms of a monatomic element:

Sulfuryl radical     Sulfuryl chloride

$$S\begin{cases} {''}O \\ {''}O \end{cases} \qquad \begin{matrix} Cl \\ S\begin{cases} {''}O \\ {''}O \end{cases} \\ Cl \end{matrix}$$

"If the sulfuryl chloride now acts on water, two HCl split off, the residue remains combined, and the resulting product can be considered

[9] *Ibid.*, pp. 124–126.

as two molecules of $H_2O$ in which two atoms of H are replaced by the group $SO_2$ [sulfuryl chloride reacts rapidly with water yielding sulfuric acid ($H_2SO_4$ or $SO_2(OH)_2$) and 2HCl].

"The manner in which the atoms are associated can be shown in a similar way for all radicals, including those which contain carbon. To do this, it is only necessary to form a picture of the nature of carbon. If only the simplest compounds of carbon are considered (marsh gas [$CH_4$], methyl chloride [$CH_3Cl$], carbon tetrachloride [$CCl_4$], chloroform [$CHCl_3$], carbonic acid [carbon dioxide, $CO_2$], phosgene gas [$COCl_2$], carbon disulfide [$CS_2$], prussic acid [HCN] etc.), it is striking that the amount of carbon which the chemist has known as the least possible, as the *atom*, always combines with four atoms of a monatomic, or two atoms of a diatomic element; that generally, the sum of the chemical [affinity] units of the elements which are bound to one atom of carbon is equal to 4. This leads to the view that carbon is *tetratomic* (or tetrabasic). . . .

"Accordingly carbon stands with the three groups of elements [monatomic, e.g. H and Cl; diatomic, O and S; triatomic, N,P] . . . as the only representative yet known of a fourth group (the compounds of boron and silicon being still too little known). Its simplest combinations with elements of the three other groups are

$$IV + 4I \qquad IV + (II + 2I) \qquad IV + 2II \qquad IV + (III + I)$$

or in examples,

CH$_4$          COCl$_2$          CO$_2$          CNH
CCl$_4$                    CS$_2$
CH$_3$Cl
CHCl$_3$

In the cases of substances which contain several atoms of carbon, one must assume that at least some of the atoms are held in the compound in the same way (as in the cases already quoted) by the affinity of the carbon, and that the carbon atoms themselves align themselves next to each other, whereby a portion of the affinity of the one carbon atom is, of course, bound by an equal portion of the affinity of the other.

"The simplest and therefore most probable case of this association of two carbon atoms is that in which one unit of affinity of the one carbon atom is combined with one unit of affinity of the other. Of the $2 \times 4$ units of affinity of the two carbon atoms, two are used in holding the two atoms together; there remain therefore six which may be held in combination by atoms of other elements. In other words the group of two carbon atoms, $C_2$, is hexatomic; it will form a compound with 6 atoms of a monatomic element, or in general with that number of atoms that will make the sum of their chemical units = 6 (e.g. ethyl hydride [ethane, $C_2H_6$], ethyl chloride [$C_2H_5Cl$], ethylene dichloride [$C_2H_4Cl_2$], 1½ carbon tetrachloride [$C_2Cl_6$], acetonitrile [$CH_3CN$], cyanogen [NCCN], acetaldehyde [$CH_3CHO$], acetyl chloride [$CH_3COCl$], glycolide, etc.).

"If more than two carbon atoms unite in the same way, the basicity of the carbon group will be increased by two units for each additional carbon atom. Thus the number of hydrogen atoms (chemical units) which may be combined with $n$ carbon atoms is expressed by

$$n (4 - 2) + 2 = 2n + 2.$$

Thus for $n = 5$, the basicity = 12."[10]    ▲

The formula of the five-carbon hydrocarbon, pentane, is accordingly $C_5H_{12}$, and the hydrocarbon series of largest hydrogen content (the alkanes or paraffins), $CH_4$, $C_2H_6$, $C_3H_8$, $C_4H_{10}$, $C_5H_{12}$, etc., do in fact fit Kekulé's series formula $C_nH_{2n+2}$ where $n$ is the number of carbon atoms.

KEKULÉ continues:

▼    "Up to this point we have assumed that all the atoms attaching themselves to carbon are held by the affinity of the carbon. It is equally conceivable, however, that in the case of polyatomic elements (O, N etc.) only a part of the affinity of these — for example, only one of the two units of affinity of the oxygen, or only one of the three units of the nitrogen — is attached to carbon; so that one of the two units of affinity of the oxygen, and two of the three units of affinity of the nitrogen, remain over and may be united with other elements. These other elements are therefore only in indirect union with the carbon, a fact which is indicated in the typical mode of writing the formulas:[11]

$$C_2H_5 \atop H \left.\right\}O \qquad C_2H_5 \atop H \left.\right\}N \qquad C_2H_3O \atop C_2H_5 \left.\right\}O \qquad C_2H_5 \atop C_2H_5 \left.\right\}N$$

[alcohol]    [ethylamine]    [ethyl acetate]    [triethylamine]    ▲

After discussing, not too successfully, the possible structures of molecules containing more carbon than permitted by the $C_nH_{2n+2}$ formula, such as benzene, $C_6H_6$, toluene, $C_7H_8$, and naphthalene, $C_{10}H_8$, and introducing a new method for classifying organic compounds, KEKULÉ concludes:

▼    "Lastly I feel bound to emphasize the point that I myself attach but a subordinate value to considerations of this kind. But since in chemistry, when there is a total lack of exact scientific principles to go on, we have to

10 Classics, pp. 126–128; translation (slightly modified) by H. M. Leicester and H. S. Klickstein, Source Book, pp. 418–420.
11 Classics, p. 128.

content ourselves for the time being with conceptions of probability and expediency, it appears appropriate that these views should be published, because they seem to me to furnish a simple and reasonably general expression precisely for the latest discoveries, and because therefore their application may perhaps conduce to the discovery of new facts."[12]    ▲

So ends the historic paper of Kekulé, without a graphical formula to help us visualize the linking of carbon atoms. He continued to *resolve* his formulas using the type formulas employed at the beginning of his paper. Only in his textbook, which first appeared in 1859, did he adopt the use of graphical representations, probably because a number of other chemists were inventing their own "pictures." Kekulé's formulas became known as "sausage formulas," such as that for ethyl chloride, $C_2H_5Cl$:

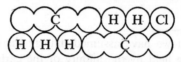

Kekulé's "sausage formula" for ethyl chloride

Kekulé expressly pointed out that the sizes of the atomic symbols, which were drawn proportionally to the valence of the atom, had no physical significance, and that the positions of the atoms as presented were not to be considered as their positions in space. These formulas make sense if affinities act vertically only. Their relation to the "typical formulas" becomes apparent if we write ethyl chloride thus:

$$
\begin{array}{c}
\text{C} \\
\lceil\text{H  H  H}\,\rfloor\,\text{H  H  Cl}\rfloor \\
\text{C}
\end{array}
$$

For acetic acid the two formulas become

and it is clear that Kekulé was only attempting to show the one-to-one correspondence of affinity units.

[12] *Ibid.*, p. 131.

## COUPER'S FORMULAS

In the same year that Kekulé's paper was published, there appeared in the *Edinburgh New Philosophical Journal,* a paper by COUPER entitled "Researches on Salicylic Acid" which contained the remarkable paragraph:

▼    "These analyses lead to the crude formula, —

$$C^7 \ H^4 \ Cl^3 \ P \ O^6$$

According to the rational theory which I seek to develop in another paper, the constitution of this body may be represented as:[13]

$$C \begin{cases} C \ldots H^2 \\ C \ldots H \end{cases} \quad \begin{array}{l}\text{It is a tertiary derivative;} \\ \text{the secondary derivative,} \\ \text{salicylic acid, being:}\end{array} \quad C \begin{cases} C \ldots H^2 \\ C \ldots H \end{cases}$$

$$C \begin{cases} C \ldots H \\ C \ldots O \ldots O \\ \vdots \\ C \begin{cases} O^2 \\ O \ldots \ldots O \end{cases} \end{cases} \Big\} P \ldots Cl^3 \qquad C \begin{cases} C \ldots H \\ C \ldots O \ldots OH \\ \vdots \\ C \begin{cases} O^2 \\ O \ldots OH \end{cases} \end{cases}$$

▲

There is no explanation whatever of the principles on which his formulas are built, but their essential character is clear. Linkages are shown between *atoms,* not groups or radicals, and carbons are linked in chains.

## PROBLEMS OF PUBLISHING A CHEMICAL THEORY

A short note by Couper entitled "On a New Chemical Theory" was presented to the French Academy of Sciences by Dumas (since only Academy members could present papers) and published a month after Kekulé's paper. The history of Couper's paper is interesting and worth noting. A 27-year-old Scotsman, who had only recently begun specializing in chemistry, he had revealed his views to Wurtz in whose laboratory he was working for Wurtz to present to the French Academy. However, Wurtz delayed its presentation till after the appearance of Kekulé's paper in Paris. Couper became very upset and seems to have shown less than gentlemanly behavior towards Wurtz, who responded by asking Couper to cease working in his laboratory. Not one to give up, it appears that Couper managed to get Dumas to sponsor his

[13] A. S. COUPER, *Edinburgh New Philosophical Journal, New Series,* **8,** 213 (1858); Alembic Club Reprint, No. 21, p. 39.

paper. The following year Couper became mentally ill and incapable of intellectual activity for the remaining thirty years of his life. In Paris it was believed that his illness stemmed from the Wurtz episode. Having published only five papers, all in the space of a single year, Couper was soon forgotten, though his views, as we shall see, played a decisive role in the development of chemistry. COUPER's important note reads as follows:

▼

"On a New Chemical Theory

"I have the honour to lay before the Academy the principal features of a new chemical theory that I propose for organic combinates.

"I go back to the elements themselves, of which I study the mutual affinities. This study is, in my opinion, sufficient for the explanation of all chemical combinates, without it being necessary to revert to unknown principles and to arbitrary generalizations.

"I distinguish two species of affinity, namely:

1°. Affinity of degree; 2°. Elective affinity.

"By affinity of degree, I mean the affinity that one element exerts upon another with which it combines in several definite proportions. I call elective affinity that which different elements exert with different intensities upon one another. Taking carbon for example, I find that it exerts its combining power in two degrees. These degrees are represented by $CO^2$ and $CO^4$, that is to say by oxide of carbon and carbonic acid [carbon monoxide, CO, and carbon dioxide, $CO_2$; Couper is using the atomic weights C = 12 and O = 8 here]. . . .

"So far as concerns its elective affinities, carbon differs from the other elements and exhibits, so to speak, a special physiognomy. The features that characterize this elective affinity of carbon are the following:

"1°. It combines with equal numbers of equivalents of hydrogen, of chlorine, of oxygen, of sulphur, etc., which can mutually replace one another so as to satisfy its combining power.

"2°. It enters into combination with itself.

"These two properties suffice, in my opinion, to explain all that is presented as characteristic by organic chemistry. I believe that the second is pointed out here for the first time. In my opinion it accounts for the important and still unexplained fact of the accumulation of molecules [atoms] of carbon in organic combinates. In these compounds where 2, 3, 4, 5, 6, etc., molecules of carbon are bound together, it is carbon which serves as link to carbon. It is not hydrogen that can bind together the elements of organic bodies. If like carbon it had the power to combine with itself, it would be possible to form the compounds $H^4Cl^4$, $H^6Cl^6$, $H^8Cl^8$."[14]    ▲

[14] A. S. COUPER, Comptes rendus de l'Académie des Sciences, **46**, 1157 (1858); trans. in Alembic Club Reprint, No. 21, p. 9, and in Classics, p. 132.

Couper now considers the case of oxygen and concludes on the basis of obscure reasoning concerning electrical properties that oxygen atoms have a strong tendency to exist in pairs. On the basis of these arguments he retains $O = 8$ for the atomic weight of oxygen and writes two linked atoms wherever Kekulé or modern chemists would write a single one with $O = 16$.

---

▼ "The highest combining power known for carbon is that of the second degree, that is to say 4. The combining power of oxygen is represented by 2. All the combinates of carbon can be referred to two types. One of these is represented by the symbol

$$n\mathrm{CM}^4,$$

and the other by the symbol

$$n\mathrm{CM}^4 - m\mathrm{M}^2$$

where m is less than n. . . . As examples of the first type, the alcohols, the fatty acids, the glycols, etc., may be cited."[15]    ▲

These general formulas of Couper were misunderstood and criticized by both Kekulé and the Russian chemist, A. M. Butlerov. By $n\mathrm{CM}^4$ Couper meant $n$ carbon atoms, each with its four combining powers wholly engaged in single union with carbon, hydrogen, oxygen, etc. Thus the hydrocarbons $CH_4$, $C_2H_6$, $C_3H_8$ and their derivatives, such as the alcohols and alkyl halides, can be referred to this type; each carbon is attached to four other atoms. Even carboxylic acids fit this scheme because the double oxygen atom permits both carbons of acetic acid, for instance, to be attached to four different atoms. An expansion of Couper's formula for acetic acid (see p. 91) would represent it as:

$$\begin{array}{c}
\mathrm{O-O-H} \\
\diagup \\
\mathrm{C-O} \\
\diagdown \; | \\
\mathrm{O} \\
| \\
\mathrm{H} \\
\diagup \\
\mathrm{C-H} \\
\diagdown \\
\mathrm{H}
\end{array}$$

However, hydrocarbons of the ethylene and butadiene series have formulas $C_2H_4$, $C_3H_6$, $C_4H_8$, etc.; $C_4H_6$, $C_5H_8$, $C_6H_{10}$, etc. These contain fewer hydrogen atoms than the previous formulas and cannot be accounted for on the earlier basis. The characteristic property of these formulas is that they lack an even number of hydrogen atoms when compared with the "saturated"

[15] *Classics*, p. 133.

compounds of the same carbon content. Affinity units are lost in pairs. Hence the type formula for these compounds is $nCM^4 - mM^2$. Couper states that $m$ must be less than $n$ presumably because no compound like $CH_2$ exists. Acetylene, $C_2H_2$, would, however, require $n = m = 2$. The loss of pairs of affinity units seems to be connected with the existence of pairs of carbon atoms. Couper was coming close to the conception of a double bond joining a pair of carbons.

COUPER continues:

▼    "Methylic alcohol [$CH_3OH$] and ethylic alcohol [$CH_3CH_2OH$] will be represented by the formulae

$$C\begin{cases} O \ldots OH \\ H^3, \end{cases} \qquad C\begin{cases} O \ldots OH \\ \vdots \\ \ldots H^2 \end{cases}$$

$$C \ldots H^3.$$

"It will easily be seen that for methylic alcohol the limit of combination of the carbon is equal to 4, the carbon in it being combined with 3 of hydrogen and with 1 of oxygen. This oxygen, of which the combining power is equal to 2, is in turn combined with another atom of oxygen, itself united to 1 of hydrogen.

"In the case of ordinary [ethyl] alcohol, each of the two atoms of carbon satisfies its combining power, on the one hand, by uniting with 3 atoms of hydrogen or of hydrogen and oxygen, and, on the other hand, by uniting with the other atom of carbon. The oxygen is combined in the same manner as in the preceding example. In these cases it will be seen that the carbon belongs to the first type, each atom being combined in the second degree.

"In propylic alcohol,

$$C\begin{cases} O \ldots OH \\ \vdots \\ H^2 \end{cases}$$

$$\vdots$$

$$C \ldots H^2$$

$$\vdots$$

$$C \ldots H^3,$$

the combining power of the atom of carbon that is situated in the middle is reduced to 2 for hydrogen, since it is combined chemically with each of the two other atoms of carbon.

"Formulae analogous to those preceding express the constitution of the other alcohols."[16]    ▲

COUPER then lists the formulas of a number of compounds such as ether, I ($C_2H_5OC_2H_5$), acetic acid, II ($CH_3CO_2H$), and oxalic acid, III $\begin{pmatrix} CO_2H \\ | \\ CO_2H \end{pmatrix}$ :

▼
$$C \begin{Bmatrix} O \dots O \\ H^2 \ H^2 \end{Bmatrix} C$$
$$\cdot \qquad \qquad \cdot$$
$$\cdot \qquad \qquad \cdot$$
$$\cdot \qquad \qquad \cdot$$
$$C \dots H^3 H^3 \dots C$$

$$C \begin{Bmatrix} O \dots OH \\ O^2 \end{Bmatrix}$$
$$\cdot$$
$$\cdot$$
$$\cdot$$
$$C \dots H^3$$

$$C \begin{Bmatrix} O \dots OH \\ O^2 \end{Bmatrix}$$
$$\cdot$$
$$\cdot$$
$$\cdot \begin{Bmatrix} O^2 \\ O \dots OH \end{Bmatrix}$$
$$C$$

I                    II                    III    ▲

These and the formula of salicylic acid mentioned earlier were the first graphical formulas of organic compounds ever published. The only earlier publication of lines in formulas representing linkages between atoms occurred in the writings of the Irishman, William Higgins (1763–1825), who in 1789 represented the oxides of nitrogen as differing from each other by the differing number of oxygen atoms contained in the molecule, his formula for the most oxygenated being:

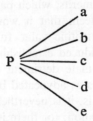

where P is a nitrogen atom and a, b, c, d, e, the atoms of oxygen.

In the papers published by Couper later that year he sometimes used solid lines instead of dots to denote linkages, and in some formulas he relinquished completely the bracket sign of Gerhardt's system. Thus for butyl alcohol he wrote the formulas shown on page 92:

[16] *Ibid.*, pp. 133–134.

$$
C \begin{cases} O\!-\!OH \\ H^2 \end{cases} \qquad\qquad C \begin{matrix} \ldots O \ldots OH \\ \ldots H^2 \end{matrix}
$$

$$
C\!-\!H^2 \qquad\qquad\quad \dot{C} \ldots H^2
$$

$$
\text{and}
$$

$$
C\!-\!H^2 \qquad\qquad\quad \dot{C} \ldots H^2
$$

$$
C\!-\!H^3 \qquad\qquad\quad \dot{C} \ldots H^3
$$

If we replace Couper's oxygen pairs by single oxygen atoms, his formulas come remarkably close to those in use today.

## THE USES OF PHILOSOPHY AND LINGUISTICS

In the paper we have just considered, there is no hint as to the mental paths by which Couper reached his amazingly advanced and clear views. His approach is revealed in a much longer paper appearing in both French and English journals:

"The end of chemistry *is its theory*. The guide in chemical research *is a theory*. It is therefore of the greatest importance to ascertain whether the theories at present adopted by chemists are adequate to the explanation of chemical phenomena, or are at least based upon the true principles which ought to regulate scientific research.

"Among those which have lately been developed, there is one, on account of its apparently numerous merits, which particularly claims investigation, and respecting which we deem that it would not be unprofitable were either new proofs of its scientific value furnished, or, on the contrary, should considerations be adduced establishing not only its inadequacy to the explanation, but its ultimate detriment to the progress of science. I allude to the system of types as advocated by Gerhardt. . . .

"Imposing as this theory is, it is nevertheless all the more necessary to submit it to a strict investigation; for there is nothing so prejudicial in the search for truth as the blind spirit of conservation. . . .

"There are two conditions which every sound theory must fulfill —

"1. It must be proved to be empirically true.

"2. It must no less be philosophically true.

"I admit that this theory is for the most part empirically true, that is to say, it is not contradicted by many of the facts of the science. Evidence that this condition is only partially fulfilled, is to be found —

"1. In the circumstance that the peroxides, for instance, do not fit very satisfactorily into the types.

"2. The principle of double decomposition cannot well be applied to the conversion of the anhydrous sulphuric acid into the hydrate of that acid by the action of one equivalent of water, the formulae of these bodies being, according to Gerhardt, in their free state $O.SO^2$ and $H^2O$. Combined, they become simply $SH^2O^4$. . . .

"The types of this theory being *essentially types* of double *decomposition,* this instance of simple combination diminishes somewhat the value of the otherwise great logical merit of this system."[17]    ▲

Couper is here pointing out, as Kekulé had done also, that simple addition reactions such as $SO_3 + H_2O = H_2SO_4$ cannot be accounted for in a system which permits only double decompositions, i.e. reactions involving exchange of parts by the two reagents.

COUPER now proceeds to a philosophical analysis, for which he was peculiarly fitted by his earlier training:

▼    "The philosophical test demands that a theory be competent to explain the greatest number of facts in the simplest possible manner.

"In applying this test, three aspects of it require to be taken into consideration:

"1. As to the extension of the theory.

"2. The explanation it affords of the facts.

"3. The manner of this explanation.

"As to the first: this theory indeed brings every chemical combinate under a certain comparative point of view with every other. Herein apparently is its merit. Nevertheless, should our test be applied to its full extent, it will be found that it is fatal to this system, in other respects so imposing. The comparative point of view which it adopts is fundamentally false.

"As to the second: it does not explain the facts at all; consequently the most essential point of the test is unfulfilled.

"3. This condition of the test is in like manner unfulfilled, from the fact of the second not being complied with.

"Why is it that Gerhardt's theory so signally fails in these two essential requisites? Because it is based upon an old but vicious principle, which has already retarded science for centuries. It begins with a generalization, and from this generalization deduces all the particular instances. But it does not come within the limits of a chemical paper to enter upon a discussion which is purely metaphysical. Nevertheless the theory of Gerhardt can only be combated upon metaphysical grounds, because it is only in overturning a general principle of research that the theory can be proposed. . . .

[17] A. S. COUPER, *The London, Edinburgh and Dublin Philosophical Magazine and Journal of Science,* [4], **16,** 104 (1858); reprinted in *Classics,* pp. 136–137.

"Should the principle which is therein adopted be applied to the common events of life, it will be found that it is simply absurd. Suppose that some one were to systematize the formation of letters into words that formed the contents of a book. Were he to begin by saying that he had discovered a *certain word which would serve as a type, and from which by substitution and double decomposition all the others are to be derived,* — that he by this means not only could form new words, but new books, and books almost *ad infinitum,* — that this word also formed an admirable point of comparison with all the others, — that in all this there were only a few difficulties, but that these might be ingeniously overcome, — he would state certainly an empirical truth. At the same time, however, his method would, judged by the light of common sense, be an absurdity. But a principle which common sense brands with absurdity, is philosophically false and a scientific blunder.

"Suppose the book that had formed the basis of this system were a German one, where all the words were found to be composed at least of two letters [Couper is pointing out that some English words only have one letter and could not possibly fit a double exchange scheme], still even in this language the viewing and systematizing of words as a series of double decompositions would be no less ridiculous.

"The sure and invincible method of arriving at every truth which the mind is capable of discovering is always one and the same. It is that, namely, of throwing away all generalization, of going back to first principles, and of letting the mind be guided by these alone. It is the same in common matters. It is the same in science. To reach the structure of words we must go back, seek out the undecomposable elements, viz. the letters, and study carefully their powers and bearing. Having ascertained these, the composition and structure of every possible word is revealed."[18]    ▲

---

This use of the word "structure" is of interest for Couper will soon apply it to molecules. He is using the word in its linguistic sense, where it does not imply geometrical or architectural arrangement but merely the order of attachment of the letters. Couper never claimed that his formulas represented the physical geometry of molecules. They were merely designed to show which atoms were attached to each other by affinity units. COUPER's language training seems to have served him well.

---

▼    "It would be well to call to recollection the parallelism of chemical research with that of every other search after truth; for it has been in overlooking this that in chemistry false and vacillating theories have been advocated and a wrong route so often pursued. In mathematics the starting point is not generalizations, but axioms, ultimate principles. In meta-

[18] *Classics,* pp. 137–139.

physics, Descartes led the way of progress by analysing till he thought he could reach some ultimate elements beyond which it was impossible for him to go, then studying their force and power, and proceeding synthetically. The recognition of this method wrought the regeneration of science and philosophy.

"On the other hand, look where Gerhardt's generalization of Williamson's generalization leads him and legitimately too — a fact which his logical spirit clearly discerned. He is led not to explain bodies according to their composition and inherent properties, but to think it necessary to restrict chemical science to the arrangement of bodies according to their decomposition, and to deny the possibility of our comprehending their molecular constitution. Can such a view tend to the advancement of science? Would it not be only rational, in accepting this veto, to renounce chemical research altogether?"[19]    ▲

COUPER now proceeds to examine other theories including the radical theory:

▼    "These reflections naturally lead to the inquiry after another theory more adequate to satisfy the just demands which can be made upon it. There is one which, as it is still supported by many distinguished chemists, cannot be passed over altogether unnoticed. It is that of the theory of certain combinates in organic chemistry which are to be viewed as analogous to, "playing the part of," inorganic elements. These are denominated radicals, and are supposed to be contained in all organic chemical products. . . .

"It is impossible here to enter upon any extensive criticism of this theory. I can only remark that it is not merely an unprofitable figure of language, but is injurious to science, inasmuch as it tends to arrest scientific inquiry by adopting the notion that these quasi elements contain some unknown and ultimate power which it is impossible to explain. It stifles inquiry at the very point where an explanation is demanded, by putting the seal of elements, of ultimate powers, on bodies which are known to be anything but this.

"Science demands the strict adherence to a principle in direct contradiction to this view. That first principle, without which research cannot advance a step, dare not be ignored; namely, that a whole is simply a derivative of its parts. As a consequence of this, it follows that it is absolutely necessary to scientific unity and research to consider these bodies as entirely derivative, and as containing no secret ultimate power whatever, and that the properties which these so-called quasi elements possess are a direct consequence of the properties of the individual elements of which they are made up. . . .

19 *Ibid.*, p. 139.

"I may now be permitted to submit a few considerations relative to a more rational theory of chemical combination. . . .

"The principle which ought to guide all research is in every case the same. It is that of analysing, till it is impossible to reach more simple elements, and of studying these elements in all their properties and powers. When all the properties and powers of the individual elements are known, then it will be possible to know the constitution of the combinates which their synthesis produces. It is necessary therefore in chemical research, in order to ascertain the various qualities and functions of the different elements,—

"1. To consider the whole of chemistry as one.

"2. To take into consideration every known combinate, and to study the character, functions, and properties displayed by each element for itself, in each of these combinates in all their different conditions and aspects. It is by a comparison of the different bodies among themselves that we are able to trace the part that is performed by each element separately.

"3. To trace the general principles common to all the elements, noting the special properties of each."[20]                                                          ▲

Seldom during the last hundred years has a scientist presented the background of his theories in as detailed and lucid a manner. His philosophical and language training guided him to the analysis of current formulas as if he were decoding an unknown language. Studying the individual elements and their frequency and locations in the different formulas, he came to the almost inevitable conclusion that carbon has two degrees of affinity, two and four, and that unlike other elements it can form stable chains.

Couper concludes his paper published in French with another pioneering proposal, the first ring formula of organic chemistry, which he proposed for cyanuric acid ($Az = N$):

$$HO—O—Az—C—AzO—OH$$

$$C \qquad \Bigg\{ \begin{array}{l} C \\ \\ C—OH \end{array}$$

$$\searrow Az$$

Thus the papers by Kekulé and Couper laid the groundwork for the structural theory of organic chemistry. It was now necessary first to search out all the manifold consequences of the theory and to test them experimentally, secondly, to discover the theory's limitations, and thirdly, probably through analysis of the limitation, to discover the reasons why the structural theory has the form it does, and to develop refinements and new theories which may more adequately account for the experimental facts.

[20] *Ibid.*, pp. 139–141.

## SUGGESTED READING

Atkinson, E. R. "The Atomic Hypothesis of William Higgins," *Journal of Chemical Education*, **17**, 3 (1940).

Benfey, O. T. "Archibald Scott Couper," in *Great Chemists*, ed. E. Farber. New York: Interscience Publishers, Inc., 1962, pp. 703–715; "Kekulé-Couper Centennial," *Journal of Chemical Education*, **36**, 319 (1959).

Brown, H. C. "Foundations of the Structural Theory," *Journal of Chemical Education*, **36**, 104 (1959).

Dobbin, L. "The Couper Quest," *Journal of Chemical Education*, **11**, 331 (1931).

Farrar, W. V., and Farrar, K. R. "Faith and Doubt: The Theory of Structure in Organic Chemistry," *Proceedings of the Chemical Society*, 285 (1959).

Walden, P. "The Problem of Duplication in Chemical Discovery," *Journal of Chemical Education*, **29**, 304 (1952). On the question of scientific duplication see also Price, D. J. *Little Science, Big Science*. New York: Columbia University Press, 1963, pp. 65ff.

# CHAPTER 10

# Epilogue

With the publication of the papers by Kekulé and Couper, the essential principles for the development of structural formulas for almost all known organic compounds were established. There were exceptions, however, as we shall see. The simultaneous enunciation of these principles by two chemists of widely divergent interests and backgrounds was a confirmation of the remarks made later by Kekulé: "Certain ideas at certain times are in the air; if one man does not enunciate them, another will do so soon afterwards." Examples of simultaneous discoveries abound in the history of science and represent an aspect of science that differentiates it from the arts. The *process* of discovery or invention, on the other hand, seems, from available evidence, to be very similar in the arts and sciences. Though not many scientists or artists have visions of the kind that Kekulé related (pages 76, 101), there is general agreement that the new insight or form or pattern comes as something *given,* as something not consciously arrived at. It comes as a sequel to intense absorption in the problem or a body of material and requires for its working out further intensive activity.

## CRITICISM OF THE NEW PROPOSALS

Though the principles of the structural theory were established, their consequences were not immediately developed, in part because of criticism of Couper's work by eminent scientists. As soon as Couper's brief paper appeared, Kekulé answered it, claiming priority for the major innovations and criticizing, owing to a misunderstanding, the symbolism ($n$CM$^4$, etc.) that Couper employed.

The Russian chemist, Butlerov,[1] who had become acquainted with Kekulé's and Couper's views during a European trip in 1857–1858, also criticized Couper's formulas as being premature and based on insufficient evidence. During the same period Kekulé and Kolbe attempted to duplicate Couper's experimental work on salicylic acid and failed. The reports of their failures cast doubt on Couper's experimental competence and it was not until decades later that Kekulé's successor at Bonn, Richard Anschütz (1852–1937), discovered that Couper's work could indeed be duplicated if his directions were followed exactly. Recent work by Pinkus, Waldrep, and Collier has again confirmed Couper's experimental skill.[2]

## FORMULAS AND ISOMERS

In 1863 Wurtz, whose strained relations with Couper have already been discussed, began to use essentially Couper's formulas (but with $O = 16$) in his lectures and the following year published them in his textbook without reference to Couper's work. At a later time he claimed that he had originated these formulas, although we now know that Wurtz had seen Couper's paper in 1858. With more justification, perhaps, it is believed that in 1864 another Scotsman, Alexander Crum Brown,[3] developed essentially modern structural formulas without prior knowledge of Couper's work. He was the first to designate every valence by a separate line as shown:

$$
\begin{array}{cc}
\text{H} \ \ \text{H} & \text{H} \ \ \text{H} \\
| \ \ \ | & | \ \ \ | \\
\text{H-C-C-Cl} & \text{H-C-C} \diagdown \\
| \ \ \ | & | \ \ \ \ \ \ \text{O} \\
\text{H} \ \ \text{Cl} & \text{H}
\end{array}
$$

ethylidene chloride (I)          acetaldehyde (II)

Originally Crum Brown drew circles around the atomic symbols but he later dropped these. The fully extended formulas simplified the prediction of isomers.

By accepting the restriction that these formulas do not represent geometrical structures but only the order of attachment of the atoms, it is clear that one,

[1] Alexander Mikhailovich Butlerov (1828–1886): Professor of Chemistry at Kazan and St. Petersburg (Leningrad), Russia, and Rector of the University of Kazan, 1860–1863. He visited Kekulé in Heidelberg and Couper in Paris and worked out in great detail the consequences of the structural theory. He contributed to the understanding of isomerism and tautomerism in organic compounds and carried out numerous organic syntheses.

[2] A. G. Pinkus, P. G. Waldrep, and W. J. Collier, "On the Structure of Couper's Compound," *Journal of Organic Chemistry,* **26**, 682 (1961).

[3] Alexander Crum Brown (1838–1922): Professor of Chemistry in Edinburgh and a student of Bunsen and Kolbe. He worked on the orientation of aromatic substitution reactions, studied alkaloids, and made important contributions to the simplification of organic formulas.

and only one, isomer of ethylidene chloride (I) can exist which must contain one chlorine on each carbon atom. This isomer is known as ethylene dichloride (III).

$$
\begin{array}{c}
\text{H} \quad \text{H} \\
| \quad\quad | \\
\text{H}-\text{C}-\text{C}-\text{H} \\
| \quad\quad | \\
\text{Cl} \quad \text{Cl}
\end{array}
$$

ethylene dichloride (III)

The existence of an isomer of acetaldehyde (vinyl alcohol) can also be pre-

$$
\begin{array}{c}
\text{H} \quad \text{H} \\
| \quad\quad | \\
\text{H}-\text{C}=\text{C}-\text{O}-\text{H}
\end{array}
$$

"vinyl alcohol"

dicted by the valence theory, but it has never been isolated; all attempts at preparing it lead to the formation of acetaldehyde (II). The inability to prepare this isomer will be discussed later. In general predictions of the number of isomers were confirmed with astounding success in the chemical laboratories. Butlerov was one of the leading figures in deducing the full consequences of the structural theory. He predicted the number of isomers of formula $C_4H_{10}$, $C_5H_{12}$, $C_4H_9OH$, etc. and assigned separate structural formulas to chemicals described in the literature. Thus began the slow process of characterizing every distinct pure chemical by its own characteristic formula.

## BUTLEROV — CHEMICAL STRUCTURES

It was Butlerov who was influential in convincing chemists that they could employ structural formulas without necessarily claiming that the formulas represented the geometrical arrangement of atoms in the undisturbed state. He differentiated between the *physical* and *chemical* structure of molecules, the latter being deducible from the products of chemical reactions whereas the former was as yet unknown. It is the *chemical* structure — the attachments of atoms as revealed by reactions — that the organic chemist could learn. Butlerov defined it as the "manner of mutual linking of the atoms in a molecule." Furthermore, he claimed that a single such structure sufficed for each chemical, whereas Kekulé was still using a number of type formulas to express different reactions for the same substance. Butlerov presented these views at a science congress in Speyer, Germany, in 1861, but at the end of his lecture he admitted that all of his ideas were essentially present in Couper's papers of 1858.

## MULTIPLE BONDS

Double and triple bonds first appeared in papers by J. Loschmidt (1861), E. Erlenmeyer (1862), and Crum Brown (1864). Erlenmeyer seems to have coined the phrase "unsaturated" for compounds containing carbon to carbon multiple bonds. The term is meant to signify that these compounds can add further atoms or groups, unlike saturated compounds that can only react by substitution. Ethylene, for instance, adds bromine readily whereas

$$\begin{array}{ccc} H & & H \\ | & & | \\ C{=}C \\ | & & | \\ H & & H \end{array} + Br_2 \rightarrow \begin{array}{ccc} & Br & Br \\ & | & | \\ H{-}C{-}C{-}H \\ & | & | \\ & H & H \end{array}$$

ethane reacts only very slowly in the absence of sunlight, and, when it does react, it liberates hydrogen bromide:

$$\begin{array}{ccc} H & H \\ | & | \\ H{-}C{-}C{-}H \\ | & | \\ H & H \end{array} + Br_2 \rightarrow \begin{array}{ccc} H & H \\ | & | \\ H{-}C{-}C{-}Br \\ | & | \\ H & H \end{array} + HBr$$

However, one large class of compounds did not seem to fit easily into the structural patterns so far developed. The "aromatic" compounds, considered as derivatives of benzene ($C_6H_6$), contained unusually small numbers of hydrogen atoms, yet did not behave as highly unsaturated compounds. Furthermore the $C_6$ unit seemed to remain intact through a vast majority of reactions. Loschmidt in his paper published in 1861 suggested that the six carbon atoms be considered as an element with a valence of 6 and wrote benzene as

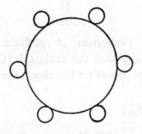

where the large circle represents the $C_6$ "element" and the small circles hydrogens.

It was left to KEKULÉ to resolve the benzene structure in accordance with the structural ideas by proposing that the six carbon atoms were linked in a ring:

---

▼    "During my stay in Ghent I resided in elegant bachelor quarters in the main thoroughfare. My study, however, faced a narrow side-alley and no daylight penetrated it. For the chemist who spends his day in the laboratory this mattered little. I was sitting writing at my textbook but the work did not progress; my thoughts were elsewhere. I turned my chair to the fire and dozed. Again the atoms were gamboling before my eyes. This time the smaller groups kept modestly in the background. My mental eye, rendered more acute by repeated visions of the kind, could now distinguish larger structures of manifold conformation: long rows, sometimes more closely fitted together, all twining and twisting in snake-line motion. But look! What was that? One of the snakes had seized hold of its own tail, and the form whirled mockingly before my eyes. As if by a flash of lightning I awoke; and this time also I spent the rest of the night in working out the consequences of the hypothesis.

"Let us learn to dream, gentlemen, then perhaps we shall find the truth. But let us beware of publishing our dreams till they have been tested by the waking understanding."[4]    ▲

By alternating the single and double bonds in the ring, all the valences in benzene could be accommodated:

benzene

Kekulé explained the isomerism of phthalic and terephthalic acids, $C_6H_4(CO_2H)_2$, by proposing that the carboxyl $(CO_2H)$ groups in the two isomers took up different positions on the ring. The accepted formulas for the two acids are

phthalic acid                  terephthalic acid

[4] F. A. KEKULÉ, *Berichte der Deutschen Chemischen Gesellschaft*, **23**, 1302 (1890); trans. by F. R. Japp in *Journal of Chemical Education*, **35**, 21 (1958).

This suggestion of positional isomerism on the benzene ring was developed by W. Koerner (1874) who showed how the different locations of substituents in disubstituted benzene derivatives could be determined. If we designate the three isomers of $C_6H_4X_2$ as

ortho            meta            para

the hexagon representing the benzene ring and unsubstituted hydrogens, then the further introduction of a group X would furnish *two* different isomers with the formula $C_6H_3X_3$, in the case of the *ortho* compound, three in the case of the *meta*, and one in the case of the *para* isomer. By separating the products of such substitution reactions, it was found possible to designate unequivocally certain isomers as being *ortho, meta,* or *para.*

*Tautomerism.* One further major victory for the simple structural theory was still in store. A number of cases were becoming known where a substance was most suitably represented by one formula for some of its reactions and by a quite different one for others. Thus at times acetoacetic ester behaved as if it were a ketone ($CH_3—C—CH_2CO_2C_2H_5$), whereas in other

$$\overset{\|}{O}$$

reactions the formula ($CH_3—C\!=\!CHCO_2C_2H_5$) of an unsaturated alcohol (an

$$\overset{|}{OH}$$

enol) seemed more suitable.

After many false answers and considerable experimental work, the riddle was solved by the discovery that in a reaction both substances were present and capable of a very rapid conversion from one form to the other if there were present a reagent that reacted with either one of them. Thus with a reagent such as hydroxylamine, $NH_2OH$, all of the material was converted into the ketonic derivative

$$CH_3—C—CH_2CO_2C_2H_5$$
$$\overset{\|}{NOH}$$

Since it was known that chemical transformations could be slowed down considerably by lowering the temperature, the two forms of acetoacetic ester were successfully isolated in 1911 by lowering the temperature to $-78°C$.[5]

[5] L. Knorr, *Berichte der Deutschen chemischen Gesellschaft,* **44,** 1138 (1911); K. H. Meyer, *Justus Liebig's Annalen der Chemie,* **380,** 220 (1911).

At this temperature the keto form is a solid while the enol form is a liquid. It was then discovered that the two forms were not spontaneously interconvertible but required a trace of basic catalyst that was normally supplied by the glass surface. By use of clean quartz vessels the separate pure forms can be kept indefinitely.

## THE LIMITATIONS OF THE STRUCTURAL THEORY

Despite the tremendous advances rendered the development of organic chemistry by the structural theory, its failures in certain areas defined its limitations. These limitations are discussed more fully in the sections which follow.

### (1) Formulas which Have No Corresponding Chemicals

The discussion of tautomerism demonstrated an important fact: a chemical corresponding to a structural formula can only be found if it can exist long enough to be detected or isolated. A structural theory that is limited only to the arrangements of atoms and does not take into account the time factor will not be able to predict the correct number of isolable isomers. Many substances characterized by very simple formulas such as vinyl alcohol, $CH_2$=$CHOH$, and by formulas with two OH or $NH_2$ groups on the same carbon atom have never been discovered. For a theory to avoid these limitations, it would need to take into account the forces of cohesion between the atoms, the strains created when certain atoms are placed in particular relationships with each other, and the ease of rearrangement into more stable molecules. Thus, whenever an attempt is made to prepare vinyl alcohol, for instance, by replacement of Cl by OH in vinyl chloride, acetaldehyde invariably results:

$$CH_2\!\!=\!\!CH \atop \hspace{0.5em}|\atop Cl \xrightarrow{OH^-} \left[ CH_2\!\!=\!\!CH \atop \hspace{0.5em}|\atop OH \right] \rightarrow CH_3\!\!-\!\!CH \atop \hspace{1em}\|\atop O$$

The vinyl alcohol does not exist for a long enough time.

### (2) One Formula — Several Chemicals: Stereochemistry

Louis Pasteur[6] in his classic studies on the optical activity of salts of tartaric acids had managed to separate two crystalline modifications of sodium

---

[6] Louis Pasteur (1822–1895): Chemist and bacteriologist; Professor at Lille and Paris. He carried out crystallographic studies and researches on fermentation, laid the foundations of bacteriology, and introduced inoculation against diseases and the "Pasteurization" of milk.

ammonium tartrate that behaved identically in almost all chemical reactions, had identical melting points, boiling points and solubilities, yet formed crystals that were nonsuperposable mirror images of each other — as the left hand is a nonsuperposable mirror image of the right hand. By contrast the mirror image of a sphere, a cube, a rectangle, or a cone is identical with its object. The latter class of compounds is called symmetrical, whereas the former is asymmetric or dissymmetric. In spite of their great similarity in properties, the two forms of sodium ammonium tartrate act as impurities on each other and lower each other's melting point owing to the disorder created by the isomeric material. Finally, if "polarized" light, i.e. light vibrating in only one plane, is passed through the tartrate crystals or their solutions in solvents, the plane of vibration of light is turned in a clockwise direction in the case of one of the isomers and in a counterclockwise direction in the other. Such chemicals that rotate the plane of polarized light are said to be optically active, and it was suggested by Pasteur that substances that retained their optical activity when dissolved in a nonoptically active solvent must owe their activity to the spatial arrangement of the atoms in the molecule. Correlating optical activity with asymmetric crystal form, PASTEUR proposed that optically active molecules must have nonsymmetrical atomic arrangements:

▼    "We know, in fact, on the one hand, that the molecular arrangements of the tartaric acids are dissymmetric, and on the other, that they are rigorously the same, with the sole difference of presenting dissymmetries in opposite directions. Are the atoms of the right [rotating clockwise] acid grouped according to the spire of a dextrorse [right-handed] helix, or placed at the summits of an irregular tetrahedron, or disposed according to such or such determined dissymmetric assemblage? We are unable to reply to these questions. But what cannot be doubted is, that there is a grouping of atoms according to an order dissymmetric to a nonsuperposable image. What is not less certain is, that the atoms of the left acid precisely realize the inverse dissymmetric grouping of this one."[7]        ▲

Pasteur thus pointed out that an irregular tetrahedron is asymmetric, but he did not attempt to apply this notion to the formulas of tartaric acid given in the literature. The suggestion that the four valences of the carbon atom should be considered as directed tetrahedrally was made by Butlerov in 1862 but not in an attempt to explain optical isomerism. He was attempting to explain the claimed chemical difference between ethyl hydride with type formula $C_2H_5$} and dimethyl $CH_3$} on structural grounds and proposed that
     H }                    $CH_3$}

[7] L. PASTEUR, *American Journal of Pharmacy*, **34**, 15 (1862).

the magnitude of the forces of affinity in the different tetrahedral directions was different. He also calculated the number of isomers expected in substituted methanes if one affinity was different from the other three, or one pair was different from the other pair. It was soon shown, however, that ethyl hydride and dimethyl were, in fact, identical and correspond to what we now call ethane, $C_2H_6$. In 1867 Kekulé again proposed a tetrahedral arrangement for the valences of carbon as an improvement on Crum Brown's two-dimensional formulas in order to permit triple bonding between carbons, as in acetylene $H-C \equiv C-H$. Two tetrahedra can be joined by sharing a face, thus

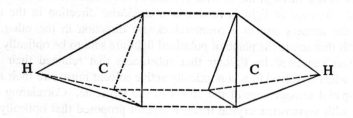

permitting three valence bonds (pointing to the corners of the tetrahedron) of one carbon to link with three of the other. It has recently been discovered that Kekulé had carefully studied and annotated Butlerov's earlier paper, so that the idea of tetrahedrally distributed valences certainly originated with the latter.

In 1873 the Dutch chemist J. H. van't Hoff[8] spent some months in Kekulé's laboratory and in the following year published a paper entitled "Proposal for the Extension of Currently Employed Structural Formulas into Space, and a Comment Regarding the Relation between Optical Rotary Power and Chemical Constitution."[9] He had been studying an article by J. A. Wislicenus[10] on the lactic acids, $CH_3CH(OH)CO_2H$, in which the latter had reiterated the view that the only difference between the two optically active forms of the acid must be the different arrangements of the atoms in space. During a walk immediately afterwards, it struck van't Hoff that four different groups attached tetrahedrally to a central carbon can be arranged in two different ways that are mirror images of each other.

[8] Jacobus Henricus van't Hoff (1852–1911): Professor of Chemistry in Amsterdam and Berlin. With le Bel he laid the foundations for organic stereochemistry. He also studied electrolytic dissociation, chemical equilibrium and reaction rates, and made detailed analyses of the mineral deposits in Stassfurt, Germany. He received the Nobel Prize in Chemistry in 1901.

[9] Cf. van't Hoff, in *Classics,* pp. 151 ff.

[10] Johannes Adolf Wislicenus (1835–1902): Professor of Chemistry in Zurich, Switzerland, and Würzburg and Leipzig, Germany. His researches helped establish the concepts of organic stereochemistry.

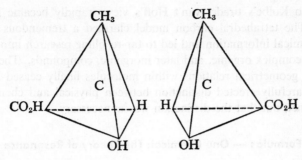

If, on the other hand, two or more groups are identical, then only a single model can be constructed. Perusing the literature, he found in fact that optical activity was normally correlated with the presence of an asymmetric carbon atom, that is, a carbon atom to which four different groups are attached. Isomers such as those for lactic acid shown above are known as stereoisomers (spatial isomers) or optical isomers. When optical activity was found but the formula was symmetrical, van't Hoff postulated (usually correctly) either an error in the formula or the presence of an optically active impurity. It is interesting to note that the postulate of an asymmetric carbon atom as the cause of optical activity was made independently and almost simultaneously by J. A. le Bel[11, 12] who had been directly influenced by Pasteur's work.

Wislicenus immediately recognized the importance of van't Hoff's article and wrote a preface to the enlarged version which appeared as a book entitled *Chemistry in Space*. This preface led Hermann Kolbe to publish a furious attack on van't Hoff's claim that it was possible to deduce the locations of atoms in space. KOLBE wrote as follows:

▼    "I would have ignored this work as I have done many others, had not a significant chemist taken it under his protection and recommended it as a worthy achievement. A Dr. J. H. van't Hoff, employed at the School of Veterinary Medicine at Utrecht, finds, so it seems, exact chemical research not to his taste. He has thought it more convenient to mount Pegasus (borrowed, no doubt, from the Veterinary School) and to proclaim in his "La Chimie dans L'Espace" how on his daring flight to the chemical Parnassus the atoms appeared to be arranged in space. . . . To criticize this paper in any detail is impossible because the play of the imagination completely forsakes the solid ground of fact and is quite incomprehensible to the sober chemist."[13]    ▲

[11] Joseph Achille le Bel (1847–1930): Chemist in Paris. He studied the stereochemistry of carbon and nitrogen compounds, fermentation processes, and the crystal forms of platinum salts.
[12] Cf. le Bel, in *Classics*, pp. 161 ff.
[13] H. KOLBE, *Journal für praktische Chemie*, [2], **15**, 473 (1877); a modified translation may be found in G. W. Wheland, *Advanced Organic Chemistry*, 3rd ed. (New York: John Wiley and Sons, Inc., 1960), p. 197.

Thanks to Kolbe's tirade, van't Hoff's views rapidly became known and accepted. The tetrahedral carbon model clarified a tremendous amount of obscure chemical information and led to far-reaching research into the spatial relations of complex organic, and later inorganic, compounds. The reluctance to speak of geometrical relations within molecules finally ceased and with it ended the carefully erected distinction between physical and chemical structure. It turned out that the distinction was unnecessary.

## (3) Several Formulas — One Chemical: The Theory of Resonance

In discussing the problem of tautomerism, we noted that at times an apparently homogeneous chemical was suitably described by more than one formula, but that, at low enough temperatures, distinct substances corresponding to these formulas could be isolated. One class of compounds, however, eluded all attempts at separation at low temperatures and seemed to pose a distinct problem. In discussing the isomerism of disubstituted benzenes we assumed the possibility of only one *ortho* isomer when in fact two can be predicted from the structural theory:

In formula I a single bond joins the carbons to which the groups X are attached, whereas a double bond links them in the second formula. No such isomerism has ever been discovered and when this case is compared with acetoacetic ester

$$CH_3-\underset{\underset{O}{\|}}{C}-CH_2CO_2C_2H_5 \rightleftarrows CH_3-\underset{\underset{OH}{|}}{C}=CHCO_2C_2H_5$$

the essential distinction becomes apparent. Tautomerism involves the complete severance of an atom (H) from a second atom and its attachment to a third. The benzene case involves no such atomic migration, but only a shifting of bonds. The fact that the latter isomerism has not been observed in nature suggests that the structural theory overemphasizes the rigidity of bonds between atoms. The *theory of resonance* postulates that when two or more valence bond structures can be written, differing only in the location of certain bonds, while the atomic positions remain essentially unchanged, then only a single substance will be found, with some of its properties intermediate between those of the structural formulas. An explanation of this failure of the structural theory had to wait for the replacement of the valence bond by an electron pair and the further understanding of electron behavior in molecular systems through quantum mechanical studies. The names most closely associated with the development of the theory of resonance are F. Arndt in Germany, C. K. Ingold and R. Robinson in England, and L. Pauling in America.

## (4) Chemicals without Structural Formulas

The final limitation of the structural theory to be discussed is an inverse statement of that presented in (1): chemicals have been discovered to which no formula or combination of formulas (cf. (3) above) corresponded. The most famous example, perhaps, is Gomberg's isolation in 1900 of the first stable organic free radical, triphenylmethyl, $(C_6H_5)_3C$, where carbon seems to use only three of its valences (cf. page 67). At higher temperatures or under more drastic conditions many other entities of abnormal valences have been discovered though most exist for only a very brief time. The fact that these entities do exist points up the temperature dependence of the structural theory, for very few tetravalent carbon compounds can be found a few hundred degrees above room temperature. But, of course, no human beings would exist at that temperature either.

## THE SIGNIFICANCE OF LIMITED SUCCESS

The limitations of the original structural theory make clear that no theory can account for all known and recognizable chemical compounds, unless it takes into consideration the dimensions of space, the factor of time, and the quantum mechanical character of matter. A molecule is not a two-dimensional symbol but a three-dimensional entity with a life history, formed at a certain time from other atomic arrangements, existing for a period in the pattern characteristic of this molecule, and changing into another entity by decomposition or reaction. Even the concept of a molecule is now seen as an invention intended to help us organize the continuous flux of human experience into meaningful patterns.

The concept of vital force, separating organic from inorganic compounds, died slowly. But organic chemistry continued to be studied essentially as an isolated discipline; hence chemists began to wonder once more whether there was perhaps something peculiar about organic compounds which differentiates them from inorganic chemicals. An answer to this view was already contained in the first volume of KEKULÉ's textbook, published in 1859:

▼    "We define organic chemistry as the chemistry of carbon compounds. In doing this, we see no opposition between organic and inorganic compounds. What has been known for a long time as organic chemistry and which more usefully may be called the chemistry of carbon compounds, is rather only a special section of pure chemistry which is dealt with separately because the large number and special importance of carbon compounds seems to make a special field of study necessary."[14]    ▲

There is disagreement today whether organic chemistry should remain a special field of study, since its principles are applied in elucidating inorganic structures and reactions and both fields require the techniques and concepts of physical chemistry for their development. Many of the most exciting research problems of today, such as the question of the origin of life and of the chemical basis of evolution, occur in the border regions between the traditional subdivisions. Scientists are needed who are thoroughly trained in several of these areas of chemistry as well as in one or more of the other sciences of physics, biology, and geology. Because few scientists have such training both in depth and breadth, much modern research is being done by teams of individuals representing the different fields of specialization.

It is hoped that this introduction to the origins of structural organic chemistry will have conveyed something of the dynamic nature of this part of chemistry. Though the subject may look polished and complete at the moment, a study of its past should quickly convince us that it is not likely to retain its present form for very long. Perhaps some of the readers of this book will contribute significantly to the next stage of its development.

[14] F. A. KEKULÉ, *Lehrbuch der Organischen Chemie* (Erlangen: 1859), I, p. 10.

## SUGGESTED READING

Campaigne, E. "The Contributions of Fritz Arndt to Resonance Theory," *Journal of Chemical Education,* **36,** 336 (1959).

Coulson, C. A. *Valence,* 2nd ed. New York: Oxford University Press, 1961.

Ihde, A. "The Unravelling of Geometric Isomerism and Tautomerism," *Journal of Chemical Education,* **36,** 330 (1959); *The Development of Modern Chemistry.* New York: Harper & Rowe, Publishers, 1964.

Ingold, C. K. *Structure and Mechanism in Organic Chemistry.* Ithaca: Cornell University Press, 1953.

Leicester, H. M. "Contributions of Butlerov to the Development of Structural Theory," *Journal of Chemical Education,* **36,** 329 (1959).

Partington, J. R. *A Short History of Chemistry,* 3rd ed. New York: Harper and Brothers, 1960.

Pauling, L. *The Nature of the Chemical Bond and the Structure of Molecules and Crystals,* 3rd ed. Ithaca: Cornell University Press, 1960.

Senior, J. K. "Evaluation of the Structural Theory of Organic Chemistry," *Journal of Chemical Education,* **12,** 409, 465 (1935); "On Certain Relations between Chemistry and Geometry," *Journal of Chemical Education,* **15,** 464 (1938).

Wheland, G. W. *Advanced Organic Chemistry,* 3rd ed. New York: John Wiley and Sons, Inc., 1960; *Resonance in Organic Chemistry.* New York: John Wiley and Sons, Inc., 1955.

# INDEX